COPING WITH
WEIGHT PROBLEMS

PAUL J. GELINAS

THE ROSEN PUBLISHING GROUP, INC.

NEW YORK

Published in 1983 by The Rosen Publishing Group, Inc.
29 East 21st Street, New York, N.Y. 10010

Copyright 1983 by Paul J. Gelinas
First Edition

Library of Congress Cataloging in Publication Data

Gelinas, Paul J.
  Coping with weight problems.

    1. Reducing—Psychological aspects.   2. Obesity—
Psychological aspects.   3. Self-perception.   I. Title.
RM222.2.G44   1983   616.3'98'0019   82-21579
ISBN 0-8239-0598-5

Manufactured in the United States of America

About the Author

2259059

Dr. Paul J. Gelinas is a psychoanalyst in private practice, a licensed psychologist, a clinical member of the New York State Psychological Association, and an accredited member of the American Association of Marriage and Family Therapists and the American Association of Sex Therapists. He is listed in *Who's Who in the East* and various other biographical directories, including the *National Register of Health Service Providers in Psychology*. The author of fifteen published books, he has taught psychology at four universities. His home town, Setauket, L.I., New York, has bestowed recognition by naming a high school for him.

Contents

PART ONE
The Problem

Introduction   3
I. *The Nature of Frustration*   7
II. *The Role of Anxiety*   17
III. *Futile Escapes*   31
IV. *The Wheel of Despair*   45

PART TWO
The Solution

V. *Forethoughts*   69
VI. *Belonging*   74
VII. *Achievement*   83
VIII. *Fear*   90
IX. *Guilt*   97
X. *Love*   105
XI. *Sex*   112
XII. *Understanding*   120
XIII. *For Those Underweight*   127

PART ONE

The Problem

A millstone and the human heart
are driven ever round;
If they have nothing else to grind
They must themselves be ground.

—Friedrich von Logau

Introduction

Perhaps many physicians could acknowledge guilt if they were courageous enough to admit their mistakes, their not infrequent lack of wisdom about a patient; to concede that people in the healing professions are, after all, human beings with limitations in spite of their extensive training. My own conscience is not entirely clear, considering that I indirectly contributed to the death of a dear girl.

And yet in a careless moment, this was brought about with the single word, "Maybe."

How could a single utterance such as that be instrumental in the destruction of a human being? To answer the question and to connect it with the theme of this book, showing its relevancy to the problem of obesity, requires looking back many years. Recently out of graduate school and comparatively naive, I accepted my first professional job. After a few weeks I became aware of a fellow worker, a girl of more than ample proportions. She seemed unhappy and lonely, and others offered only that condescension and second-hand cordiality that are so often resented by fat people.

Out of sympathy, I befriended her. As the months passed the relationship, on my part based on pity, became to her mind more than mere friendship. Certainly any notion of romance was far from my thoughts. Nevertheless her tentative approaches, unwarranted praise, and obvious devotion all combined to declare that she was indeed strongly attracted to me.

Her round face, almost angelic in beauty and kindness,

glowed as we discussed my work. My narcissistic self absorbed her admiration. But as a love object, she was nonexistent. I refused to reconcile ugliness of body with the beauty of her intellect and giving nature.

Endless was her devotion as she talked of my career and the brilliant future that she predicted for me. All of this I accepted in my young self-centered way, giving little in return, enjoying her company because she fed my unsteady ego. She was ever ready to help, writing clinical reports for me, standing up for me in seminars and public meetings, editing articles for submission to professional journals. When one of these was accepted for publication, we celebrated with a restaurant dinner and champagne. I did wish that I could be more grateful, but basically I only took her kindness for granted, even then dreaming of slim and sensuous women far removed from the obese one who failed to create any sense of feminine allure.

Many months later, after she had been particularly helpful in extricating me from a difficult situation, I put my arms about her. "Thanks," I said. "Why are you always with me when I need you?"

She rested her head on my shoulder. "It's because I love you," she said simply, raising moist eyes to mine, silently pleading. Then she added, "If I were not fat, would you, could you love me?"

Suddenly I wished to be free of her, but I recoiled at the thought of hurting her. How could I possibly crush her hopes.

"Maybe," I said.

She subsequently tried one diet after another, losing a few pounds, then going on binges of eating in cyclical defeats. Soon, however, I had reasons for rejoicing. My career brightened with an overseas appointment. Through her tears, she expressed happiness for me as she clutched the dozen red roses I gave her before my departure.

Her letters followed me with implied reminders that the word "Maybe" had indeed contained a promise. However, the pressure of work and other interests gradually led to neglect in answering her letters. By the final months of my three-year assignment I had almost forgotten her, particularly since the girl of my dreams had come into my life.

In my long absence this good friend had become overwhelmed. Taking a profusion of pills, she had indeed managed to lose weight. But when at last she acquired an acceptable figure, she found herself unable to adjust to normal eating habits. In fact she had developed a compulsion against food, an uncontrolled urge to avoid nourishment, nauseated into getting thinner and thinner, degenerating into extreme emaciation until her heart could no longer withstand the strain. Never again to pursue a futile hope, she had embraced anorexia nervosa and death.

The years and decades flowed on with greater demands of my profession, almost erasing the guilt, the tender regrets. Sympathy for the problems of people with weight disturbances nevertheless remained. But they seemed out of my field; as a psychotherapist I dealt only with the human mind, not the body.

Without purposeful observation, however, it finally became clear that fat persons who consulted me for emotional problems and subsequently were rid of their neuroses through therapy actually in most instances lost weight. Ultimately they took greater pride in their appearance, losing weight with no obvious effort of will nor the torments generally associated with programs of weight reduction.

The women often acquired better figures and a new and

frequently buoyant outlook on life, becoming more feminine and attractive, no longer slaves to an eating compulsion. Men similarly were often transformed as a disap-
pearing paunch signaled renewed masculinity and physical
pride. Not all were so changed, but enough to represent
firm evidence that weight control lay primarily in the realm
of psychology. To lose weight, I concluded, required first
the removal of serious frustrations, of anxiety, thus releas-
ing one's power to meet needs and desires.

Thus in this circuitous and experiential manner was
evolved the concept of the self-help method described in
this book. It does not imply a promise based on mere impulse, but encouragement to the forty million men and
women who are statistically overweight in the United
States. Will it work for you?

Maybe.

Chapter 1

The Nature of Frustration

Excessive weight may be due to slight psychological illness, a mental propensity with neurotic characteristics. First, it should be evident that emotional disturbances—except perhaps psychosis—arise from frustration, the inability to meet one's basic needs. The blocking of a person's wants is the primary cause of emotional difficulties. This applies to all neuroses, a category in which belongs compulsive eating.

Overweight therefore can be deemed a psychological aberration caused by unhappiness and the torments of unmet needs.

No one who is happy, fulfilled, and free of anxiety ever suffers serious and debilitating emotional disturbances. Life is good and satisfying and therefore free of self-destructive tendencies. Many clinical psychologists, however, consider overweight to be the product of a discontented state of mind.

The problem, of course, varies from mild resentment of a few extra pounds to more serious instances of obesity. In each case, however, the cause is frustrations arising within the self or from the environment.

What are these needs that, if denied or left unsatisfied, initiate discomfort, including unwanted fat? People are gregarious; they need a sense of belonging not only based on a desire for friendship but also linked with a primitive and age-old urge for self-preservation. One feels safer in groups, among friends. The individual also has the will to achieve as a means of establishing identity in his own eyes and in those of fellow human creatures. Also sought is freedom from fear and guilt. The person wants to understand the world, which seems ever more complicated if not directly threatening. And finally, who does not yearn for love and affection?

Young people deprived of a combination of their needs become antisocial, in sad rebellion, mentally deranged and alienated, with the potential for developing various neuroses. Unfulfilled and dejected, teenagers commit suicide at the rate of 25,000 a year; and psychiatrists assert that for each one who succeeds in ending his life, fifty others have made an unsuccessful attempt at self-destruction.

Perhaps it may seem far-fetched to link compulsive eating with these dire statistics. But, as our argument unfolds, it will become clear that overweight is frequently woven in lighter shades in the tapestry of frustration. An unhappy person will often behave destructively: neglecting the person; allowing degeneration in a desperate giving up, a rejection of self-worth and personal pride; often choosing overindulgence and consuming food as if somehow the hurt and alienation will be lessened.

With increasing frustration, the person feels that life has fallen far short of his expectations. Buffeted by conscious and subconscious yearnings, one often in conflict with another, he or she becomes confused, defeated, and unhappy. And behind this situation lurks a deepening anxiety, a nervousness, that seems to cast a pall over surroundings and social life, a miasma of negative attitudes with hope held only by a thin thread.

The blocking of needs, then, is the essence of frustration. And from the nonsuccess coupled with anxiety and worry emerge neurotic trends. At this point, the mind, the ego, seeks freedom from the anxiety. Unfortunately in many instances the defenses thus selected are self-defeating, such as choosing overeating to assuage the pervasive uneasiness.

Since frustration is the direct result of inability to meet the needs for happiness, it becomes advantageous to examine more closely the nature of frustration and its consequences, particularly as it bears on the weight problem.

Conscious Frustrations

To say that many young people are not happy is to suggest that they are possessed by severe frustration of basic needs. The dream of beckoning years has not infrequently been dimmed by bafflement and delusions. Different adjustments and aspirations are required; our values must be reexamined in a fast-changing society. Conscious and obvious frustrations abound, reaching our minds through the mass media, as television, movies, magazines, and newspapers predominantly stress discord in our country and throughout the world.

In psychotherapy, the patient must examine his weaknesses and the obstacles that stand in the way of confronting his troubles before it becomes possible to utilize powers against them and ultimately to attain a blossoming personal growth and adjustment. Similarly, if our minds are allowed to bravely face the negative elements that beset us, we can avoid defeats and attain a better life by getting rid of that objectionable fat.

At this point, however, we need not look within ourselves for hidden or subconscious frustrations. Enough of them threaten us like encircling mountains perhaps ready to belch volcanic debris upon our unprotected heads.

The conscious frustrations are varied and can be viewed without effort on our part. Picture the social diseases, the divorces and subsequent aging with no one to care, the alcoholism, and the lack of direction. Imagine struggling mothers who have borne children out of wedlock, pregnant teenagers, victims of welfare, and the drug addicts. If we could lift the roofs of hospitals, mental institutions, jails; if we could peer into discordant homes with the abused children, the brooding and frequent anger exploding there. But wide publicity about overeating and drug abuse, anorexia nervosa, and other dangers tends to create added anxiety, restricting even our freedom of choice, keeping us from the compulsion to go to hell if we wish to do so. And along with the countless other frustrations, crime is becoming a serious cause of worry, polarizing those who demand a more severe judicial system and restoration of capital punishment and those who argue that greater sympathy is required to tame the criminal element. In fact, our nation is gripped by endless indecisions, and major depression is prevalent in both men and women.

And so we grow fat, gobbling food as a respite, perhaps also in rebellion—in any case, seeking to overfeed the body because we are not happy. The individual feels an overall dissatisfaction, absence of successes, inadequacy, lack of love—and boredom.

A case in point illustrating marital frustrations is that of Lucille, eighteen years old, and her husband, Ted, seven years her senior, after two years of marriage. The union had taken place thoughtlessly and without any firm commitments. Ted, a handsome, carefree type, wanted sex without having to frequent singles bars. It would be nice, he concluded, to go to baseball games, watch TV together, afterward going to bed, kidding around, laughing, loving, followed by peaceful slumber.

Unfortunately, the attraction soon faded, and Lucille, a vivacious brunette, high-spirited, gradually began to put on weight to offset her boredom. For some time she had felt abandoned emotionally by her husband. Their disagreements grew acrimonious as she acknowledged that her figure had become too plump for her husband's taste. Still, Lucille clung to her man even when he turned off the light and turned his back, leaving her empty and deserted. Gazing blankly into the darkness, with her husband already asleep, she knew that there had never been any real love between them. Indeed, Ted was always sought after for parties and other social events while generally she took second place, laughing with the others at his antics, his flirting with any pretty girl.

Then and there that night, alone with bitter thoughts, she made her decision. The marriage had been a failure from the start, she realized. She would leave him, go to college or business school with the help of her parents, have a career, look forward to a life of her own—and become a person again.

Lucille had felt mounting frustration. However, she managed at last to confront it bravely without too unbearable anxiety, thus avoiding more pernicious distresses had she surrendered to her mistake.

Subconscious Frustrations

The obstacles and hindrances encountered in our daily lives are easily distinguished. These are the frustrations related directly to the environment and to the people who make up our milieu. But there are others no less influential in our mental state of being. We now refer to the subconscious frustrations that arise often without our awareness from the depths of ourselves. These are also the culprits in emotional difficulties that often lead to the slide into overweight.

What is the nature of the mysterious and generally misunderstood frustrations that tend to steer our behavior without our knowledge or voluntary direction? Very often they steer us to unwise actions or decisions—even to self-destruction.

It should be emphasized that we never entirely obliterate any past experience, its fantasies or shocks. Memories may seem to be erased, forgotten, lost in the passage of time. However, these past events and emotions have not actually disappeared. They still lie in our subconscious, most of them repressed deep within us.

Like an iceberg with only about ten percent above the waves, the bulk of the ice below the surface, our mental life is frequently hidden from conscious mental processes. Even though it may seem that some past experiences have never existed, actually they only await the opportunity to find expression, generally indirectly and seemingly unconnected with the original experiences and pain of long ago.

An oversimplified example is that of Elizabeth, a twenty-six-year-old woman who was deathly afraid of dogs. She could not recall ever being harmed by a dog. Nevertheless she panicked even at the sight of a miniature poodle and sought to avoid contact with dogs at almost any cost.

Only a combination of free association and age regression under hypnosis finally brought out what had been imbedded in her subconscious. She had been only three years old when she had witnessed a terrifying event. Having been forbidden to leave the backyard, she had nevertheless wandered into the street in front of the house and begun petting a dog. Her mother, fearing for the child's safety, had run toward her shouting, "Don't touch that dog—it might bite you." The animal, doubtless expecting an attack from the excited woman, had growled and bitten her as she shook the little girl.

Seized with fear, guilty for having disobeyed, and seeing blood on her mother's arm, the child had suffered shock. The psychological trauma was so severe that her conscious mind rejected it, repressed it in the years that followed until therapeutic means finally brought to conscious level what had been for so long buried in her subconscious.

More illustrative would be the girl whose overweight was based on the subconscious fear of competing with her mother—becoming fat and unattractive as a defense against an unacceptable wish.

Excessive frustrations cause a long list of actual neuroses and personality disorders, including phobias, obsessional behavior, free-floating anxiety, unexplained fears, depression, bizarre ways of responding to people, guilt, self-hate, and a host of emotional upsets, including conversion hysteria as described below.

Why a given person chooses a particular kind of neurotic symptoms as a reaction to frustration is not known. Many factors may determine that choice. The reason one person develops paranoid ways while another displays harmful sexual dysfunctions or a compulsion for overeating is possibly based on a variety of subconscious factors, particularly those linked with early childhood experiences and emotions.

Conversion Hysteria

In this emotional disorder, the person's frustration results in bodily changes, organic deficiencies as an indirect expression of inner conflicts. For example, the person who feels guilty about a heinous crime against a loved one may develop paralysis. A young child who peeks surreptitiously at his naked mother and is severely punished may in later years suffer temporary blurring of vision when the compulsion to see women in the nude is reawakened. The threat of forgotten punishment surges to the surface.

Similarly, overweight may be a form of conversion hysteria, a specific way of responding to frustrations and their resultant emotional discomfort.

A person under serious stress may develop any other of the classified neurotic tendencies. But the fat person, through his own psychic makeup, has subconsciously selected overweight as a response to disappointments. The process will be further elaborated in succeeding chapters, detailing the course of degeneration leading to obesity.

However, it would be unfair and certainly unjustified to brand all fat people as neurotics. As indicated earlier, there may be glandular or organic reasons. We speak of neurotic tendencies in the average overweight person, and not necessarily of deep-seated mental illness. Most problems of weight control can be solved through insight and self-help. Obesity is generally tinged with neurotic leanings, particularly because it reflects conduct that is self-defeating, one of the common characteristics of all neuroses.

It should be observed that frustration is not always a villain. Life would be empty without obstacles to overcome, the competition of existence on every side, the challenge of a worthy opponent in sports, the joy of treading water against the resistance of the waves, the correction of weaknesses. The human race would probably not have survived had frustrations and struggle not existed to build up our strength. The human being in primordial times was possibly the weakest in the survival race. He learned, as you are now doing, to use his brain in battle with stronger animals. All about him were huge creatures, reptiles, enormous beasts ready to crush him. Primitive man, his mate, and his children trembled in damp and gloomy caves, ever aware that dangers lurked in the night. Beset by frustration and anxiety, man was therefore compelled to sharpen his wits and finally to defeat the threats against his survival, emerging as ruler of the animal kingdom.

In modern life even walking is in fact the coordination of movements against frustration. Each step is a struggle against gravity and the imminence of falling. We cannot therefore say that all frustrations must be eliminated. Certainly not—since that would be impossible.

There will always be obstacles to overcome and in the process to build up our capacity to cope. On the other hand, there is no danger that recurring frustrations will disappear, since anyone with absolutely no frustrations would be dead.

However, we are dealing specifically with oversevere frustrations that result in overweight when a person reacts against a problem that hitherto could not be mastered or controlled. Allowing oneself to become too heavy is a self-defeating way of avoiding painful feelings, anxiety, guilt, shame, or a deep sense of inadequacy.

Unconquered and chronic frustrations of this sort are generally accompanied by anxiety, worry, nervousness, and a poor sense of self-worth. These, then, are the emotions that we wish to escape. And unwisely we may choose overeating as a means of running away, instead of confronting the problem in a more rational manner.

It has been pointed out that there are two types of frustration, sometimes overlapping. Although subconscious frustrations are more deeply embedded than conscious frustrations, both are treated with the same procedure, namely, behavioral therapy for self-help. Failure to understand one's frustrations and their origins does not interfere with the efficacy of reward and punishment, the basis of the method herein described and recommended.

However, we have explained the nature of the two types of frustration in order to counter a person who might say, "Yes, I'm overweight, but I have no frustrations. I have everything I need, a good home, fond parents, people who are kind to me. It's true that I am nervous, unhappy, and I can't stop stuffing my mouth—but frustrations? I have none."

In such an instance, there are subconscious conflicts beyond the individual's awareness that need to be lessened through constructive habits and ways of thinking. Severe frustration must be removed regardless of origin or degree of awareness. With new motivation and understanding the problem tends to be solved, making it easier to overcome the discomfort and possibly the lingering shame of being different from one's ideal of slimness.

There is an effective way to overcome the chronic frustrations that cause overweight. This method will be described in the second part of this book in a manner easily followed to reach permanent solution of the weight problem.

The Role of Anxiety

Now that we have examined frustration as the primary source or cause of overweight, it must be observed that the long-term blocking of one's needs is inevitably accompanied by anxiety, a sense of restlessness and unhappiness. In fact, anxiety is an indicator, a warning, pointing out that frustration is at work, that our needs are being denied or unfulfilled.

Since anxiety, a state of tension and worry, is an intermediate stage between discomfort and frustration, it must be evident that in attacking anxiety itself we have chosen the lesser enemy, one that is a mere spear carrier for frustration.

Once anxiety has set in, the person who is unaware that frustration is the root cause of the anxiety tries desperately to get rid of the anxiety itself—overlooking the real source of the trouble. That is generally the neurotic's way of seeking a solution. But often it is self-defeating behavior that has little effect on the weight problem.

Are we actually saying that all the exercises, the diets flooding the market are worthless, that in the end they do not work? You may counter, "I know someone who has lost twenty pounds on a strict diet, and she looks wonderful." Of course that happens frequently, or the thousands of cookbooks and diet regimes would not attract so many followers. However, it involves a constant and unending

17

struggle, a battle with oneself ever renewed. Many fall by the wayside, giving up the tug-of-war in resignation, yielding to overweight particularly when new tensions appear upon the scene.

Lest you assume, however, that the validity of the author's contentions may be in question, let us observe a short case history of a man whose compulsion was to consume vast quantities of food in almost any form. Like other overweight victims, he certainly wanted to change the habit that was wrecking his life and happiness.

Jim Wilson came to my office, a bearded man, rugged-faced, with challenging eyes. "I don't know why I'm here," he muttered as he plunked himself in the chair opposite my desk.

I looked at him without responding, awaiting a winding down of his tension.

"Its my physician—he sent me." He leaned forward with difficulty, adjusting a strap on his boot.

"I know," I said softly. "His secretary called, saying you wanted an appointment."

"All right," he admitted. But his shock of hair seemed to complete the picture of rebelliousness and pervading hostility. "Well," he added, "what do you want me to do—damn it, I don't need a shrink."

"Why are you here?"

"Listen," he responded to my question. "I can't stop eating. I lose some when I diet, but it's all useless."

I learned to pity the strange man, even gradually as the weeks passed to like him for courage, if not for his poor judgment.

In order for Wilson to appreciate his real predicament, it was necessary for him to identify the areas of his needs, the desires that had been stifled and denied.

Picture this man, son of unfortunate parents whose minds

had been twisted by adversity, indifference, and cruelty. The farm mother waddled in her gloomy kitchen, feeling the sins of the world upon her shoulders, praying for perdition on all who followed the demon pleasure. Even bad thoughts must be punished, she admonished her child, while her husband, penniless and hopeless, swilled food, red-eyed, hostile, and threatening, beating his son as if he were an animal. The pudgy youngster cried in the night, not knowing that other kinds of life existed, yet searching hungrily for some vague hope, some response to his yearning for life.

How many of his needs were unmet during those sad, empty years? Many of them were blocked or had little chance to see the light. Of these, the desire for love and tenderness was paramount, even though he had no suspicion of what he really lacked.

In any case, this man, now an adult, had to embark on a course of self-discovery and the gradual fulfillment of basic wants before he could find peace within himself. A man or woman can be starved for affection, some degree of recognition, and other needs without awareness of their absence. It is then that some people can become beastly, self-destructive, with happiness ever beyond their reach like a distant mirage.

In some cases the overweight person goes on a strict diet, treating what he believes to be the source of his trouble. But he is merely wrestling with the symptom and not the missing needs themselves. Instead of concentrating on the reduction of weight, he should first remove the frustrations that are the cause of the problem. It is frustration that gives rise to anxiety. The obese person feels that he has found a way to relieve anxiety by eating.

Wilson's efforts to follow one diet after another were unwise because his relative abstention from food always resulted in greater anxiety. Having repeatedly managed to lose weight, it was as if each time he had been robbed of his security blanket, was no longer protected by his defense.

The frustrations that lay behind his obesity also triggered countless disasters, arrests, lost jobs, altercations with superiors, a court martial while in the armed forces, a broken marriage, and two children left behind although he loved them. Certainly the man had many reasons for remorse, guilt, despair—not to mention the ever-present anxiety.

All this he believed had been caused by a great restlessness. And certainly but indirectly it appeared that he was right in that conclusion. In a moment of determination, he joined a national organization specializing in problems of weight control, and he succeeded in becoming a moderate eater. But after a period of elation, he realized that his anxiety had returned and held him even more fiercely than before.

He had made the mistake of attacking anxiety itself as the direct origin of his trouble instead of the frustrations that engendered it. Had he first removed the frustrations that caused the anxiety, he could then have greatly benefited by giving up his harmful overeating. His obesity and the anxiety were symptoms, not the disease itself.

However, since anxiety is the handmaiden of unmet needs, of frustration, it becomes necessary to examine its mechanism in order to gain greater understanding of the weight problem.

Anxiety is an important concept in psychology. It plays a vital role in the development of personality and its functioning. It serves as a red light warning of danger, a signal that a person is deprived of needs for efficient and satisfactory operation. The red light in traffic indicates that danger lies ahead if the motorist persists in acting in a given manner. Anxiety is similarly a signal declaring a threat to the organism if the person allows the present situation to persist. Anxiety says, "I make you feel bad because there is something lacking in your life, because certain needs are unmet, denied."

A further example might be a motor low in lubricant or oil. The machine runs with difficulty and, as in severe neurosis, may actually come to a stop. Similarly, the person who is in short supply of things that he needs may function poorly, sometimes even having a nervous breakdown.

Anxiety comes upon the scene, saying, "Hey there, listen to me. There is something wrong here, and you'd better pay attention to some basic needs that must be met—do something about yourself."

And the person generally reacts in a variety of ways, struggling to escape the uneasiness. Unfortunately the action taken is frequently focused on the anxiety, a choice of a neurotic nature. Such self-defeating devices seldom work in the long run. Although tension may be lessened by strong drink or an orgy of eating, the anxiety soon returns to gnaw at nerves and being. In the next chapter, these ineffective ways of combatting anxiety will be examined in order that you may understand them and if possible guard against harmful maneuvers.

Anxiety is a painful emotional experience. It engenders excitation in the internal organs of the body. In fact, the glands, muscles, nerves, and blood circulation are mobilized for a fight. Primitive man utilized this readiness for combat when confronting a bear, another attacking animal, or a human enemy. He acted directly against frustrations and dangers, thus removing the reason for the continuation of anxiety.

In a civilized community, although the possibility of physical harm still exists, the frustrations are generally of a psychological nature. Among the frustrations are lack of love and of self-respect and inadequate achievement. Nevertheless our unmet needs bring about similar mobilization of the physiological apparatus. The organism is ready to fight against obstacles, but the obstacles are unseen and hard to identify. Accordingly, there is a tendency to focus on anxiety rather than its cause. The result is often that the lack of fulfillment remains to haunt the victim. The body is ready to tackle the problem, to fight. But the man or woman is like a rider trying to go in all directions at the same time. The consequence is the choice of the wrong object for attention, while the real culprit escapes. A man may choose, for example, to jog three times weekly to relieve his tension, not realizing that if he sought to achieve something worthwhile for himself and his fellowmen he would not suffer the anxiety in the first place. The overweight woman may go on a strict diet to relieve the anxiety that her appearance causes her, not understanding that in choosing obesity to allay anxiety she has merely postponed it.

The state of anxiety can be experienced as pain, depression, melancholy, and tension. There is no such thing as subconscious anxiety, any more than pain can be experienced without being aware of it. One, of course, can be unaware of the reason for his discomfort; but he cannot be unaware of feeling it.

There are three types of anxiety: reality anxiety, neurotic anxiety, and moral anxiety. These do not differ in the degree of pain and suffering experienced; all are equally unpleasant. They differ only in the nature of their source, the specific frustrations involved.

The three types of anxiety may be further described as

follows: 1) fear of the external world, such as anticipating the loss of a job; 2) fear of one's own drive, such as sexual lack of control; and 3) fear of other people's opinion and their moral criteria.

The person who experiences anxiety is not necessarily aware of the type involved. He may think that he is afraid of knives or guns in the outside world whereas actually he may fear his own aggression, the subconscious urge to hurt someone. Or he may think he is afraid of high places as a threat in the external environment, when in actuality he is afraid of his own conscience that might impel him to jump as a punishment for past or present guilt feelings. An anxiety state may therefore have several sources that blend into a mixture of the three types of anxiety. In any case, each or a combination of them serves to alert him to danger.

Reality Anxiety

This is a signal that danger exists in the external world, outside the inner self. It is a condition that threatens harm. One is afraid of poisonous snakes, a vehicle out of control, a criminal with a gun.

While these are objectively frightening, in some people an added factor may be present: environmental conditioning from others. For example, one may have absorbed fear of darkness from parents. Some psychologists say that such environmental fears are inherited because past generations were constantly imperiled in darkness before fire and light were available to them. It might more reasonably be assumed that forgotten childhood experiences of fright during the night proved traumatic.

In any case, fears are easily engendered in the child when he is not strong enough to cope with danger. At times he can be overwhelmed by fears. His body is flooded by stimulations. His heart beats faster. Breathing more rapidly, his whole organism is tense because he is unable to handle the frustrations, helplessly awaiting he knows not what. Childhood experiences of this nature leave a clinging network of fears in an adult, particularly when he is reduced to the child's helplessness and finds the original anxiety reignited.

When it is impossible to remove anxiety by getting at the frustrations involved, the anxiety keeps increasing until the person becomes confused and further tormented, sometimes with tragic results. Fortunately there are means of avoiding or reversing the dilemma, as we shall see in Part Two of this book. Further evidence will be presented to show that getting rid of fat is not in itself an effective or viable way to allay anxiety, since the overweight only creates additional anxieties.

Neurotic Anxiety

This type is characterized by a fear of instinctual drives, the fear particularly of one's own sexual or aggressive urges that have not found a suitable outlet, building up frustrations. It is estimated that in many prisons 90 percent of inmates have sexual problems, not to mention the misdirected aggression that led to their conviction. This type of anxiety is linked to a free-floating apprehension. The victim is always expecting something awful to happen. It can be assumed that such a man or woman is afraid not of his own shadow but rather of his unacceptable drives and desires.

The anxiety neurosis may find expression in intense fear of some object or situation out of all proportion to the actual danger. The victim of a phobia may be afraid of crowds, open spaces, enclosed areas, mice, even light bulbs, or a host of other objects or conditions. In each case, the fear seems utterly unreasonable; it springs from within the self and not from the outside.

Always a phobia represents a subconscious temptation associated with aggressive or sexual drives. Behind every phobia there is a repressed wish for something that is considered forbidden. The person wants to acquire a forbidden realization or object that he fears and denies and that later becomes associated with a given phobia.

A woman, for example, was unreasonably afraid of elevators. An examination of the hidden dynamics of the fear revealed that as a little girl she had suffered shock and trauma that became disguised in the phobia. At an early age, riding in an elevator with her parents and her younger sister, of whom she was extremely jealous, she had partially and temporarily blinded the sister with a blow from a toy. Subsequently she was severely punished. She seemed to have lost her father's devotion, and she felt guilty for the death wish toward her sister. Years later, the incident repressed, the prospect of riding in an elevator reawakened the hidden desire to destroy her sister, an act from which she shrank.

A phobia may be intensified by a moral conflict. In that case the feared object is linked to something morally forbidden, as for example the woman who has an intense fear of being assaulted. This, in a reasonable degree, is normal. But when the fear is so strong that the woman sees a potential attacker in every man, thus limiting her functioning outside the home as well as with her family, a phobia seems definitely indicated. Strangely, the woman may secretly desire to be overwhelmed, but she cannot accept this possibility and accordingly shifts the secret urge to the phobia. The inner self says, "I want it," but the conscious self says, "That's terrible—I am afraid to think of this awful thing." Consequently the fear and conflicting desire are pushed down out of consciousness, transferred to the phobia—where it is ever ready to warn indirectly against the deep secret.

Another form of neurotic anxiety is characterized by panic explosions. The action then occurring has the nature of "going berserk." The disturbed person may shoot or stab others indiscriminately. After the episode, the person is at a loss to explain the violence except to say that something seemed to explode within him.

Generally the mentally ill person has been known as "a nice guy," withdrawn and harmless. However, the truth is that there had built up in him over a long time various frustrations that ultimately led to deep anxiety. The tension had finally sought sudden discharge.

Panic behavior is sometimes displayed in less violent forms. It becomes evident when a seemingly meek person utters obscenities, steals on impulse, or otherwise acts on uncontrolled urges. The chronic frustrations are thus relieved in a sudden burst of unacceptable acts. Laws are broken by otherwise respectable people because of similar pressures. After such outbreaks of impulsive behavior, a sense of relief is felt temporarily.

Such impulsive action generally arouses a threatening reaction from others. At the very least the person is considered unstable. In his serious aberrations, people turn away from him and otherwise create situations that only add to the original tension. Similarly, some people invite obesity as self-punishment from a sense of guilt.

Harry, indeed, was a person who had felt this tightening up, a tension that would not let go. Always he had been highly disciplined, thoughtful of others, controlled and meek on the job. He felt nevertheless that if things became more pressing he might explode into doing something awful.

With some difficulty he was persuaded to join an encounter group where a not too wise psychologist urged his patients to express their feelings at all costs, particularly their hostility. Being highly suggestible, Harry practically overnight became oblivious of the concerns of others. He was now a man, he told himself. He spoke loudly. From being meek he became a boor, his unreasonable demands alienating others. The group had convinced him that to be aggressive was the secret of freedom and peace of mind.

And he did feel better for the time being—except that his colleagues shunned him. His wife, at the end of her patience, finally threw up her hands and said: "You've become mean and despicable."

With his new sense of independence and daring, he barged into his boss's office demanding a raise in salary. He was fired. The brief satisfaction of expressing unreasonable aggression brought retribution in social backlash.

The encounter leader had failed to realize that Harry's prior meekness and bottled-up feelings were mere symptoms of unmet needs. Harry had attacked the anxiety rather than the deeper frustrations that were basic to his problems. This, again, was a neurotic attempt that could not work—just as the fat person puts on weight as a futile means of escaping anxiety.

The average person, too, experiences neurotic anxiety, but it does not affect his life in the pernicious way that it does the seriously emotionally disturbed. It is true, however, that the difference between the normal person and the tense neurotic is one of degree, and the borderline between the two is often shadowy.

Moral Anxiety

This category of anxiety is felt as guilt and shame. It is engendered by a danger originating in the conscience. The conscience is the agent or representative of the parents. In other words, the sense of right and wrong has been implanted in the subconscious by authority figures. Again and again the command is given as if the conscience were playing a tape repeatedly. Doing or even thinking something that transgresses the taboos previously recorded by parents arouses anxiety. The perfectionism thus absorbed during childhood serves as a scale of values for the victim. It has long ago become firmly set in the personality, and the person cannot escape the feeling of guilt by running away from it. The conflict between the desire to meet some justifiable needs is opposed by subconscious compulsion rooted in the moral principles of the parents. Almost unbearable tension and ambivalence are the results. The struggle is not with the outside world. It is within the person, based upon the lingering fear of the parents or other authority figures. The influences are the direct results of the disciplinary code inculcated by the parents, principally directed against sexual and aggressive impulses. Consequently the conscience limits or prohibits sensuality and disobedience.

This pattern of conduct creates a paradox. The virtuous person feels more shame than the less virtuous. How can a person who is "sinless" feel greater guilt than a more liberal one? The answer must be that he who abstains from sexual activities or aggressive acts tends to be bottled up, feeling more tense because his needs are frustrated. Even the mere thinking or fantasizing about the forbidden things leaves him more inclined to tension. Such a person of excessive self-control is more susceptible to temptation and tends to be plagued with instinctual urges.

This tendency was exemplified by a middle-aged woman of ample proportions whose passion was to war against prostitution. She traveled widely to address women's groups, damning so-called ladies of the night, demanding that prostitutes be punished severely, their names broadcast, and their clients be treated with equal severity. She lobbied legislators, wrote lengthy articles for magazines and newspapers, pleading that children be protected from the influence of this evil. She seemed a saint to the like-minded, sacrificing her life to her crusade. Unfortunately under the stress of her all-embracing task, she succumbed to what is euphemistically called a nervous breakdown.

Whether or not her aim was justified is irrelevant to our discussion. The fact is that she suffered moral anxiety so severe that she devoted her whole career to fighting that anxiety.

Guilt feelings are the price paid by the overidealistic person. Conscience-stricken, he transgresses by even thinking or dreaming something that is against his moral code.

It has been observed that anxiety is a warning. The discomfort alerts the person that something harmful is happening to him. He is being deprived of some need. Actually he is afraid of fear, the fear of ever-mounting tension every time his thoughts wander to the forbidden.

The guilt feeling may become so unbearable that the anguished person actually seeks punishment to allay the torment. A criminal in this category will unconsciously leave clues to assure being caught; a philandering husband will provide evidence for his wife to discover his adultery. And strangest of all, whenever a heinous crime is committed and widely publicized, the police are deluged with false confessions. The possibility of going to prison for a crime not committed is less painful than the anxiety itself.

The fat person overeats as a means of escaping one or more of these anxieties. He has been led into the trap of assuming that by handling his troubled state of mind by overeating, he will become free of anxiety, boredom, and unhappiness. The defense of excessive indulgence does not work in the long run. The frustrations that aroused anxiety and dissatisfaction still exist. Accordingly, dieting without first removing the frustrations likewise fails. Dieting may succeed for a time, but the fat will ultimately return because the devil of frustration is still crouched within, awaiting weak moments when in desperation you stuff your stomach again.

Futile Escapes

The person caught in the mesh of anxieties already described is unhappy. His life is filled with foreboding, fears, and a general sense of uneasiness. Unfortunately he often chooses a neurotic means of escape that is self-defeating and unworkable.

As previously stressed, the frustration that arouses anxiety is something that has blocked the way to peace of mind, to meeting one's real needs. The person is frustrated when he is deprived of a goal not yet found in the environment or not within his reach because of ignorance or unwise action.

Let us examine some of the psychological devices used in futile attempts to escape from anxiety caused by frustration.

Narcissistic Identification

Sigmund Freud spoke of self-love, using the word narcissistic taken from the myth of Narcissus, who fell in love with his own image reflected in a pool of water. We therefore say that a person is afflicted with narcissism when he devotes an inordinate amount of time and attention to admiring himself. Other people's opinions are excluded. He already has such a high estimate of himself that nothing seemingly can shake his self-admiration.

If the narcissism is sufficiently strong, the man cannot be attracted by the average woman because she cannot reflect a picture of himself, his essential love object; the woman similarly afflicted cannot choose a male object that is alien to her own self-image. Here we have a possible answer as to why some people turn to homosexuality, or why a man is drawn to a masculine woman or a woman marries a man with distinct signs of femininity.

David was not too well liked. Although overweight and flabby, he dressed in the latest styles and expensively. The son of a successful physician, he attended the best schools, followed by trips to Europe and other far places. But he had no real friends. He was little interested in the opposite sex, except to receive their praise as his just due. He seemed to disdain those who commented on his many advantages. Owning a powerful sports car, he brushed aside the warnings of his father about careless and daring driving, an admonition that was proved valid when he had a serious accident that left him facially scarred. It was easy to handle the resultant financial claims, but the previously proud young man was left with an altered face to haunt him.

His narcissism was threatened, and he sank into a deep depression, particularly because he feared plastic surgery, afraid of further mutilation of his body. He became almost completely withdrawn except for sharply limited contacts with his parents. As an only child, he had been pampered and endowed with anything he desired. But his self-love was now shattered. The world had ceased to feed his ego to reenforce his shaky self-admiration that now seemed so vital to restore his self-centeredness.

His father finally realized his duty to suggest psychological help in order to avoid the possibility of a more serious tragedy. Accordingly, the nattily dressed young man walked into the psychologist's office, his facial scars partially covered with cosmetics. Soft-spoken, correct, and distinct in speech, he said that the accident had disturbed him greatly and he felt that his father was right that he needed treatment to get rid of his depression.

Many months later he had gradually come to understand that the trauma of the accident was reflected not only in his defacement but in the fear of plastic surgery. Subconsciously both of these factors were a part of a deeper fear, the fear of castration, which was directly tied to hostile feelings toward his father. The young man could never dare identify with the father. As a consequence he had chosen femininity as a defense against masculinity. He could not hope to compete with his father, a strong, steady, and admired man. The masculine mold was too challenging and unreachable for him to compete successfully. He had fled emotionally from the contest because early in life he had assumed that his father's calm courage, his strength, coolness, and prominence were threatening and impossible to imitate. He was vaguely aware of the frustration, but he had not even thought of confronting the seemingly impossible task of overcoming the obstructions to his well-being. He had retreated into baby fat, seeking to recapture earlier and more pampered indulgence.

The major task of anyone is the handling of his frustrations that result in anxiety. Many people manage to adopt realistic problem-solving. Others are not so fortunate. For example, the person who is inclined to overweight may continue to use ineffective ways of trying to get rid of the fat that arouses anxiety. Yet that anxiety is compounded after repeated failures to reduce because the core of the difficulty lies in frustrations, not in the anxiety itself. Such futile attempts usually fail. It is as if a person dodges an oncoming train by stepping onto an adjacent track where an equal disaster looms in the other direction.

Repression

This psychological device removes the forbidden desires from consciousness so that they seem no longer to exist. Being out of awareness, the taboo wishes seemingly are unable to evoke anxiety. However, the repressed material tends to become conscious indirectly; it attaches itself to something that appears harmless, which then becomes associated with the repressed material. This useless attempt to avoid anxiety leads to renewed anxiety, imbued with the same qualities as the original anxiety.

For instance, an obese woman is made nervous and anxious by her appearance. She manages to repress the discomfort, accepting her dilemma. But strangely she becomes afraid of cats. A black cat arouses anxiety similar to the original anxiety because in some mysterious way it has been shunted to the ordinarily harmless object. From being made anxious by the fatness itself, which was repressed, she is now the victim of an unreasonable fear. Indeed, we do not eliminate a forbidden idea by forgetting about it. It retaliates by seizing another object that was previously harmless but now becomes anxiety-producing. The primary frustration, accompanied by its inevitable anxiety, must find expression one way or another regardless of how one may seek to escape and disguise the consequences.

You cannot unwind the frustrations connected with being overweight by rationalization or by tackling the problem by means of repression.

Overrepressed people convey the impression of being withdrawn, rigid, and guarded. They expend so much energy to maintain their repressions, holding down the forbidden thoughts and actions, that they have little energy left to enjoy themselves, to communicate with other people, and to handle their environment effectively.

Sometimes repression interferes with the health and functions of the body. Because of fear of sex, for example, a man may become impotent, and a woman frigid. Many physicians and psychologists associate repression with such illnesses as arthritis, ulcers, and asthma.

A child who has repressed hostility against his parents may find himself turning against society itself as the repressed idea breaks through another channel. Perhaps the child becomes a juvenile delinquent, rebelling against the world in general. Also the overrepressed person may turn the hostility against himself, even committing suicide as self-punishment—not to mention the less drastic choice of obesity.

Repression can be eliminated by confronting the frustrations and thus eradicating the anxiety that motivated the repression as a secondary means of defense. This is not accomplished automatically. It occurs only after the danger posed by frustration has been effectively disposed of.

When the person has acquired sufficient strength and understanding to cope with the blocked desires and needs, repression is no longer necessary. The person can now use his energy to mold his life toward a more realistic and successful handling of the environment and of his body.

Projection

This psychological mechanism tries to relieve a person's anxiety by blaming something or someone for his unwanted fat. If a person feels unbearable tension due to an uncontrolled weight problem, he may attribute it to the external world rather than himself. Instead of saying, "I'm too heavy," he can blame the food distributors with their junk products, additives, and too liberal use of sugar. In that manner the attempt is made to project the origin of anxiety onto others.

The person who fears his own aggressive or sexual urges may seek consolation by thinking that it is his neighbor who is promiscuous and inclined to violence instead of himself. That is why some people see nothing but evil in others. Minorities are too active sexually or ever ready with aggressive acts, they conclude. Such an attitude is a convenient way of alleviating one's guilt or hostility.

The aim of this attitude is to shift an internal danger to the external world to make it easier to handle. It is less difficult to deal with something outside oneself than to cope with anxiety of subjective origin. Projection thus helps at least temporarily to alleviate anxiety. Convinced that others are persecuting him, the person feels free to attack his imaginary enemies, deeming himself justified in hating them. He gets satisfaction without feeling guilty for his own hostile impulses. Of course, this is all a devious maneuver for evading personal responsibility.

A case in point is that of Marie, a high school student, who was some twenty pounds overweight. After the seesaw of various diets, she had finally given up, concluding that she could never hope for an acceptable figure and the attention of the opposite sex. She had read a newspaper article to the effect that in some instances the mother's habit of forcing food on her child inculcated a compulsion to overeat in adulthood. The body had been trained to demand more nourishment for its functioning, and the mind like a tape recording insisted on more and more food. Another feature story had asserted that obesity was largely inherited, that one's genes were geared to overweight.

Accordingly, in her effort to avoid self-responsibility, Marie now projected her anxiety to her mother. It was she who was to blame. Marie even imagined that her mother still was determined to keep her fat because of concern with her health when periodically she tried another diet. Gradually she developed hatred for her mother, heaping upon the older woman the blame for her discouragement and unhappiness.

Of course, Marie's dilemma could be resolved only by identifying the real frustration and eliminating it. The obesity certainly was a symptom of a deeper psychological problem. Seeking to project her anxiety onto her mother held no possibility of overcoming her basic difficulty.

Projection as a defense mechanism is frequently encouraged in early childhood. The child soon learns that he can escape punishment and self-blame by finding excuses for his transgressions. When the defense works, he is in effect rewarded for telling a lie. He thus forms the habit of projection to avoid self-responsibility for his failure to control his eating habits.

Reaction Formation

Our instincts are arranged in pairs. Love and hate, life and death, dominance versus passivity, construction versus destruction are examples of such paired opposites. When a frustration produces anxiety, the person may seek to get rid of it by sidetracking the offensive impulse to its opposite. For example, a person who hates another may end by loving him to hide the hostility. The dynamics by which a given feeling is hidden by its opposite is known as a reaction formation. The mechanism in the obese person takes the form of admiring fatness instead of detesting it.

A recent play depicted the device when a victim of rape

found herself in love with her attacker. Is this the mental process that leads a woman to remain deeply attached to a brutal husband, staying with him despite abuse? Yes, in the minds of some emotionally disturbed people, it is safer to love a dangerous person than to hate him. Love thus becomes a defense against a feared object or person. Being attracted by obesity may be acceptance of an enemy as a defense against it.

The case of Debra further illustrates the utilization of reaction formation in a futile attempt to sidetrack obesity. Thirty-six years old, she was a former winner of beauty contests. After years of marriage and two children, she discovered that her husband had cooled toward her and that even the children preferred their father. It occurred to her that her figure, though not yet obese, merely chubby, needed rejuvenating to hold her husband's love.

However, Debra, like so many in her predicament, discovered that exercise and dieting are difficult to maintain over a long period of time. After many months of first losing weight, then overeating again, swinging back and forth from torture to self-indulgence, gradually despair set in, and finally resignation.

There was a limit to her endurance. Following a minor operation, she pampered herself during her recuperation. Feeling justified in self-pity, she stuffed herself with sweets and junk food. She deserved to rest, she rationalized, and she deserved her husband's sympathy after her illness. She extended her helplessness, realizing that her husband paid more attention to her when she complained of pain and discouragement. Meanwhile her chubbiness degenerated into obesity.

Gradually, her hatred of fat took a turn in the opposite direction. She began to say that fat was beautiful. The great painter Rubens had been attracted to voluptuous women.

Now she wanted to be fat, proclaiming the many advantages to all who would listen. Obese people were loved for their good nature, their ability to enjoy a joke, the jolliness of their nature.

Debra had chosen the opposite of her previous detestation to avoid the anxiety created by being overweight. Of course, the reaction formation did not work, and her husband was further alienated. She had chosen the wrong method of attacking her anxiety. Had she worked directly toward getting the love and respect she desired, she might have succeeded in meeting her essential need.

It is interesting to note the difference between two kinds of love. What is true love? How can you distinguish between real love and one that is based on reaction formation?

Reactive love is exaggerated. The lover protests too much. He is extravagant in expressing his love, affected, and showy. The love is false and is usually easily detected as counterfeit. Too hasty a marriage motivated by reaction formation generally is headed for failure.

Reactive love is similar to the headlong decision to lose weight, plunging into crash diets, expecting too much too soon without taking the time to understand the basic reason for the weight problem.

Sometimes a reaction formation satisfies the original desire. A husband, for example, may not admit even to himself that he resents his wife. Under the pretext of concern for her, the overprotection becomes a form of punishment. Similarly an overweight woman, resenting her husband, blaming him for her anxiety, may under the pretext of concern for his welfare and health impose fattening food upon him as a subconscious means of punishment.

Reaction formation, whether it operates in justifying overweight or in other forms, serves a hypocritical purpose.

It makes the person rigid and inflexible. It cannot serve to eradicate the frustrations behind the anxieties.

Fixation

Some people who have a problem with weight control are suspected of being fixated in their psychological development. Emotional progress in most people is a gradual and continuous development during the first twenty years of life. There are four stages in this evolution: infancy, childhood, adolescence, and adulthood. The average person passes through these stages without too great difficulty.

With some persons, however, this procession of development comes to a halt at a certain stage or lingers on a lower rung of the ladder. We refer to such a person as being stunted in his emotional growth. He has remained fixated at an immature level, handling part of his environment as if he were still an infant. His fat remains, with a symbolic baby spoon feeding his hungry baby mouth.

Fixation, like the other defenses already described, is a means of protecting oneself against anxiety. It is largely ineffective because, again, it fails to confront the frustrations that caused the anxiety.

The fixated person is fearful of taking the next step in his development. He cannot nor does he desire to face the obstacles and hardships that may be ahead. The fixation of the overweight person tends to be on the oral level. The obtaining of nourishment was the first channel through which the infant gratified his well-being. Upon eating and drinking depended security, the warmth and odor of the mother's body, the coziness, and the very survival.

Perhaps deep in our subconscious, we wish at times to return to the serenity, the delicious dependency partially retained by the fixated person. On the adult level this is impossible for the average person without gradually becoming completely defenseless against the demands of the world. However, within all of us there is that almost mystical longing for inertia without demands, for being fed by an all-enfolding mother in the womb of contentment.

Imagine the baby nurtured at the maternal breast, the crying ceased at last, the environment fading; now only somnolence lulls as though swinging softly on a star, ensconced in the cradle of a mother's protective arms. This peaceful sleep must thereafter be the prototype of most contentment and happiness.

Little wonder that some persons under severe stress seek a regression to this cocoon of warmth and dependency; little wonder that the fixated person so tenaciously seeks to hold on to the blissful state.

But the fat and pampered baby—now an adult "baby"— whose oral needs continue excessively is a tragic example of inability to adapt to reality. The fixation proves to be a counterfeit of the original state. In fact, the excess flesh in the fixated individual hinders him from functioning in a society that he views fearfully as a threatening jungle. Change and emotional maturity can mean unpredictable dangers that he is reluctant to envisage or confront.

Fixation is early evident and emphatic at any threat of separation from the mother. The chubby child holds on desperately to the mother figure. The first year of school, for example, arouses all kinds of anxiety. The child exhibits panic at entering new surroundings, at the bustle of others, the presumed menace of a teacher taking the place of the mother.

For the fixated person, each step up the ladder of development tends to be traumatic. The adolescent trembles on his first date, the high school graduate looks forward to work or college with trepidation, the college years are followed by the uncertainty of the world of work, and marriage is viewed not as a challenge, but rather as a dilemma of indecision. Each step, each new venture, arouses anxiety. He leaves the old and familiar with perturbation, tension, and expectations of disaster. When the separation anxiety becomes too great, he clings ever more tenaciously to the earlier fixation.

What does the fixated person really fear? What are the dangers that prevent his psychological development? What are the awful possibilities of change and the threats of the future? What are the impulses that drive the overweight person to choose obesity, the oral gratifications that take the form of eating as the main source of satisfaction?

The fixated person is afraid of failure, insecurity, and punishment. Fear of failure implies fear not only of possible painful outcome, but also of being blamed or possibly ridiculed for inadequacy. Fear of insecurity is a state of mind that abhors the demands of new situations. Fear of punishment is based on parents' negative reactions to the child's attempts to attain some degree of independence.

A child who feels secure, who is treated with dignity by parents who are not overpunitive, is unlikely to become fixated at any stage of development and consequently has less likelihood of having a later weight problem.

Regression

This is a return to an earlier stage of emotional development. It has been pointed out that the fixated person has made no progress in his psychological evolution. The regressed person, on the contrary, has moved up the ladder, but under stress he has returned to an earlier rung. An adult may respond like an infant, seeking a defense in childish behavior when the world presses too heavily on his shoulders. Having reached a reasonable norm of emotional stability, nevertheless the person reverts to an earlier mode of reacting through the mechanism of regression, perhaps deciding that it is safer to let himself become fat and dependent rather than slim and independent.

Mable, a fourteen-year-old, demonstrated in her behavior a regression that followed a series of traumatic events. Her father, whom she had worshiped, had committed suicide. She had found him dead, and she recalled with great bitterness the discord and quarrels that had pervaded the household. She blamed her mother for the tragedy.

Weeks later, her mother brought home a lover, who ensconced himself as part of the household. Mable seethed with anger, also feeling rejected and despairing. She now spent most of her time almost in a daze, listening to her favorite records but finding some consolation in stuffing herself with food. Biting her nails, she seemed transported almost to the infant stage, at times giggling then crying. Still she gorged herself until she became grotesque, a bloated figure sucking her thumb. She had sunk into a deep regression because of inability to withstand her cruel, uncaring environment. Only when her paternal grandmother managed to convince the mother that Mable needed new surroundings did she begin to regain her health, as love and affection became available during the period of her grief and mourning.

Although Mable's regression was unusually severe, even the average person is not free from milder, recurring regression. People smoke, drink strong liquor, chew gum, overeat, and do countless things of an oral and regressive nature. At one time or other most of us return to infantile practices in attempts to evade tension. The security of infancy, when there was no need for responsibility and self-control, always seems to beckon on the subconscious level.

Any of the defenses discussed may be invoked in vain attempts to ward off anxiety—including the state of obesity. All of them are irrational ways of dealing with anxiety, because each hides, denies, or postpones confrontation of reality and causative frustrations. The concomitant distortions hinder psychological development. The energy used to maintain a defense—maintaining excessive weight, for instance—leaves little energy for effective solution to a given problem. Finally, if the defense fails, the result may be a nervous breakdown, depression, or a deeper form of emotional disturbance.

Chapter **IV**

The Wheel of Despair

The problem of weight control frequently involves the employment of various defenses and useless endeavors to overcome the anxiety connected with it. The dilemma is inextricably linked to the complexity of the more serious neurosis. Accordingly, the torments of the overweight follow the course generally seen in the better-known neurotic illnesses.

The mental and emotional processes of the overweight vary in intensity and often follow a downward progression, depending on the severity of the anxiety. The Wheel of Despair delineates the degeneration of the struggle against anxiety. The victim builds up additional defenses upon the failure of prior defenses until greater despair emerges.

The Wheel of Despair is symbolic, representing a series of turns on an axle to the next spoke in a sequence of emotional states. Imagine the wheel slowly turning, each advance indicating a worsening of the problem. Each turn on the axle is an attempted defense against the previous one, further aggravating the problem rather than lessening it.

Let us follow the deepening crisis of Annette, a pretty coed of nineteen, ample of figure but symmetrical, whose frustrations led her to a sad predicament.

Frustration It is the nature of human beings to satisfy physical and psychological needs in order to achieve peace of mind and even survival. Annette as a college freshman felt frustrated particularly because she seemed unable to make friends. While other girls had plenty of dates, she did not, even though she knew that her appearance was as good as that of many of her classmates, if not better.

She was the only child of a broken marriage, and she had looked forward to college as an escape from her mother, a professional singer. Her mother always sought to be the center of attention and resented any suggestion that her daughter might be able to surpass her own charm. She spoke disparagingly when Annette's bosom gradually developed more amply than her own rather small breasts. Annette had never been able really to communicate with her vain and self-centered mother.

The divorced father had remarried and moved to California, far removed from Annette's Long Island home. However, he had volunteered to pay his daughter's college expenses. One of her morbid worries was that she might fail in her studies, thus disappointing her father. In her fantasy, she would be a credit to him; someday he would receive her with open arms and take her away from so much that was disagreeable in the present.

Annette could not remember harmony at home. Before the separation, her father, a busy lawyer, had little time for her except for frequent gifts and a hug and a kiss as he hastened to keep appointments. Yet, with the passing years, she continued to love him dearly and dreamed of living with him and his second wife. The hope was bluntly squashed by her angry mother: "Your father abandoned you; he doesn't want you—his wife would hate you." Casting a disdainful glance at her daughter, she added, "I'm providing for you—you're an ungrateful brat."

Poor Annette—she so wanted to be loved, and yet her rigidity and inability to be spontaneous conveyed a distant coldness that was readily interpreted as snobbery. She moved about the campus laden with books, an aloof look in her dark eyes. Before the end of the first semester, her roommate moved, mumbling the excuse that a close friend wanted her to move in. "Don't feel bad," the girl said. "I think you're a wonderful person to share a pad with." Annette stopped her. "I know," she said, "I'm just a bore—and I know it."

Anxiety   The frustrations and anxiety were piling up at compound interest. Annette did get a date, but in her insecurity she did not know what to talk about with the young man. Hesitantly she sought to converse about the Lake poets—Shelley, Wordsworth—while he talked about the Beatles and the Rolling Stones.

After a few beers at the Purple Moon, he walked her back to the dorm and, without trying to kiss her, left with a cool goodnight. Annette later sat gazing from her window at the foggy night and began to cry, wondering what was wrong with her. After a long period of confusion and sadness, suddenly she felt hungry. She wiped away her tears, gulped down one stale donut after another, then consumed almost a whole box of chocolates. Finally, benumbed, she slipped into bed, feeling stuffed and ready for sleep and oblivion.

In the second semester, time passed in a sort of splendid isolation. She didn't care; alone in her room, she stuffed herself with cheese, cold meats, and candy, hardly noticing that she was putting on more and more weight. She seemed perpetually hungry even after having ample meals in the cafeteria. Poring over books, she let her imagination take flight into the ethereal world of the great writers.

And now her ambition was to get A's in her courses, particularly in literature. That would please her father, who had written short poems for her when she was a child. But still anxiety impaled her, would not let her go. It was a free-floating anxiety, unspecific now. Eating nevertheless was a means of muting the tension.

She plunged into her work, completely absorbed in studies, memorizing poetry, and composing numerous essays. Her compulsive eating seemed to moderate. But later, in the second half of the sophomore year, she received a further jolt.

Anger   A young instructor in English literature pranced behind a lectern condescendingly waving a scented handkerchief for silence. He proceeded week after week to pontificate on his favorite authors, examining the symbolic and psychoanalytic implications of their work.

The reviews and criticisms demanded of students had to reflect his bias in order to receive even a passing mark. After being given a C for a composition over which she had labored long and hard, Annette became increasingly disillusioned and confused. She remained sullen and silent in class. Nevertheless she read Freud assiduously, though repelled by the sexual emphasis. The concepts of psychoanalysis left her cold. One day she heard her name called and tensed at the intrusion upon her thoughts.

"Miss—Annette," the instructor called from the front of the room. "Will you come forward?"

Annette arose from a back seat and approached, holding her breath, bewildered.

"Is this your composition?" he asked dryly.

She put out a trembling hand for her paper. "It is mine . . . ." She noted a D at the top above a scribbled message from the instructor.

He said mockingly, "Read the words underlined in red pencil."

Still confused and bitterly wondering why he was submitting her to such humiliation before the class, she read the underlined phrase, ". . . the man who we saw . . ."

"Read that again," he ordered. "Louder."

"Yes, sir," she submitted.

But the sadistic man continued his goading. "You've been here for more than two years," he added, his mouth twisted in derision. "Are you so ignorant of elementary grammar?"

Annette quickly recognized the mistake, feeling shame mounting within her. Then a sudden anger seized her as she gazed at the instructor. "How dare you?" she exploded, tossed the papers in his face, and flounced out of the room.

Alone in her room at last, she heaped curses upon the instructor, pacing back and forth, letting the anger spread to the very tips of her fingers. Somehow, strangely, she felt better, the anxiety slowly oozing out of her. She had never felt such hostility, and she thought bitterly of bringing charges against the man through channels available to students who felt unjustly used by a member of the faculty.

That night she did not feel hungry.

It seemed that her anger and the determination to seek revenge had a therapeutic effect. She derived a sense of satisfaction in the thought of inflicting proper punishment upon the despised enemy. She was not horrified at the fantasy of plunging a knife into his heart, watching the blood flow from the feminine man-beast.

In fitful sleep a dream emerged, terrifying in the night. A huge insect appeared, and she found herself desperately and maniacally torturing it, pulling off its wings, deriving ecstasy from the harm she was inflicting. She gouged its eyes, pounded its body with a hammer as she felt delight in its anguish. Finally it was dead, but the eyes remained open. She shoved her thumbs in the sockets to shut off the stare, then turned her back and folded her arms, still glorying in her cruelty. It seemed she had paid back—extracted just punishment for all the hurt, the rejections, and the injustices of the past. With a last kick at the mutilated apparition, she started to walk away, but paused to take a final look at the havoc she had caused. However, the creature had disappeared.

Quiet A cloud passed over the pallid moon, and she was alone, lost in a vast space without end. A voice re-echoed reproachfully from nowhere. "Guilt," said the voice, "is the price you must pay for your sin of anger and hate."

"Who—what—who is speaking?" she shouted at the invisible phantom.

"I am your conscience."

"I have no conscience," she countered. "And I hate you, too."

Finally she awakened bathed in sweat.

A weak sun reached tentatively through the dormitory window, and Annette heard the morning stirring in the hall as from a great distance. A miasma held her to the pillow as she struggled to gain a toehold on reality. Where was she? The room seemed nebulous and receding. She grappled with the void, and the world gradually began to take shape, the concept of space and time.

Annette left her bed and dressed mechanically, feeling an undefined guilt linked to the dream, which had been real enough. It was as if she had committed some atrocious crime, though she refused to know or to admit its nature and details. But the guilt was gnawing, imbedded in her mind. Was her guilt due to the explosive incident in the

Literature class? She pondered, then reasoned that she had indeed been justified, but was he really at fault? Was she within her rights in becoming so angry? After all, she had been careless in using the nominative case instead of the accusative. The stalemate still held her as she showered and later brushed her dark hair from troubled eyes—troubled and indecisive.

An hour later she walked across the campus, mechanically moving among fellow students. The guilt remained, eating further into her being. Only an apology would set her free. And as she thought of the decision, her steps quickened and she felt the anxiety slip from her as through a sieve.

During class, she found herself sympathizing with Lady MacBeth who couldn't wash the blood from her hands. When the bell rang, the students filed out amid bantering and laughter. Finally, Annette walked to the front of the room and confronted the instructor.

"Sir," she ventured.

He turned his head and grinned condescendingly. "Yes," he said. "What do you want?" he added coldly, shuffling papers.

"I'd like to talk to you," she said weakly.

He laughed. "Well, my chubby friend," he said, letting his eyes sweep her from head to feet. "I thought fat little girls were better natured."

Annette grew darkly red and felt despairingly that he had flung scalding water over her head to slowly sink into the fat of her body. But the words came out in spite of the shame and humiliation. "I want to apologize," she blurted out, standing there as if expecting a blow.

The man gathered his notes, stuffed them into the briefcase, cast one last disdainful glance at her, and walked out without another word.

Annette stood motionless in the empty room, feeling devastated, both very small and very large—small in spirit, too large physically. Who could love her, forgive her, a "fat little girl"? She could not cry, the dagger had plunged too deeply into her flesh. The din and trampling of student feet, the high voices in the adjacent hall were like a web strangling her. A radio blared from somewhere. Annette was alone—very much alone.

Self-hate   The next turn in Annette's Wheel of Despair was that of self-hatred. Suddenly her detestation of her body was almost unbearable. She determined to go on a near-starvation diet. Her fantasy dealt with stripping off the excess fat as if it were a lethal garment that must be shed at all costs. She blamed herself not only for her overweight, but also for all the indignities implied or directly inflicted. She now hated the very sight of her image in the mirror. Minimum eating was finally viewed as a sort of punishment that she deserved and must bear for past stupidity, for petty anger, and the hostility that had served as a flimsy defense. Examining her naked figure, she suddenly knew that it was she who had been at fault. An acid illusion penetrated her consciousness. She did not want to die because then the self-punishment would be denied. She had been condemned to torture and must bear the cross of her suffering as a just sentence for past sins that were all the heavier because they could not be specifically identified.

With the passing months the flesh melted, and in the lassitude that now held her she combed her long black hair singing under her breath the sad songs of the lost. She felt like a saint bearing her burden with morbid pleasure in the suffering.

Even her father's occasional and impersonal letters were cast aside unanswered because she felt unworthy of anyone's love and affection. The enemy, which was the flesh, had joined hands as a means of casting out the whole world—with her self-hatred festering within the core of her. Most of her classes were skipped, assignments neglected. Nothing mattered. She had lost sixteen pounds on carrots, clear soups, and crackers. Her fierce determination had triumphed, reducing the weight and at the same time punishing herself.

At midyear, however, she failed all her courses. Drawn and pale, she responded to a summons from the guidance office. A tall counselor with kind eyes waved her to a chair opposite his desk.

"Can I help you?" he inquired softly. "You seem to be in trouble academically."

"I know," she replied dully. "I've been trying to lose weight—somehow my studies escaped me."

He looked at her sympathetically. "How long since you have had a real meal?"

"Isn't it enough that I'm overcoming my weight problem?"

"It's a worthy cause to improve oneself." He hesitated. "But what about your health? Possibly you feel too tired to study. Is being thin worth destroying yourself?"

"I don't care," she blurted out. "What right have you got to tell me what to do?"

"None whatsoever—your dignity must always be preserved through self-responsibility." He came around the desk, took her hand. "I'd like to help you, but now is not the time to talk about your grades. Do me a favor, Annette, go back to your dormitory, have a good meal, and I'll see you again next Thursday, same hour. You are a

fine girl, sensitive and intelligent. Believe me, I understand your problem.'' He pressed his hand more firmly on
hers; it was warm and gentle.

It had been so long since she could recall someone like
this counselor who spoke softly, not reproachfully, saying
that she was a fine girl. Her step was lighter. Later she ate
a meal that sent a stream of energy through her weakened
body. She had forgotten how wonderful it was to eat with
peace of mind. Finally she dallied over coffee and a piece
of mince pie with the treasured ice-cream topping. This
was the nectar of the gods, and every mouthful must be
enjoyed with no thought of the future.

A slim girl sat down opposite Annette. Although her
eyes were heavy and somewhat distraught, she seemed
friendly enough. In her present mood of elation, Annette
started a conversation. At one point, she asked, ''How in
the world do you keep your beautiful figure?''

The stranger laughed a little and put two fingers to the
back of her mouth. ''This way,'' she said shortly.

''Tell me— please tell me,'' Annette begged.

''Like some others—I model sometimes; I've got to keep
my figure.''

''What do you mean 'like others'? You've just eaten all
kinds of fattening things.''

''Well, I like to eat. I fill up, enjoy every bite until I'm
ready to burst, full up to the gills—then I go to my room,
shove fingers down my throat, and throw up.''

''It works?'' Annette began, but the girl picked up her
empty tray.

''See you later,'' she flung over her shoulder, walking
away.

At that moment Annette fell into the jaws of a trap that
has snared many who are addicted to food, especially junk

food of high calories and little nutrient value. It is called bulimia in the medical profession, coined from the Greek words for "ox" and "hunger." The condition is on the verge of becoming epidemic among girls in their twenties, often among those of prestigious background.

The victims are generally subject to societal pressures to remain thin. But they continue to be obsessed with food to a point at which they hardly think of anything else. Preventing them from establishing love and other personal relationships, the food itself serves as a defense against loneliness.

The process that Annette had eagerly grasped as an answer to her problem involved eating as much as she desired, then disgorging the food. After a binge, she purged her system by self-induced vomiting. Although the practice enabled her to remain in college for the rest of the year, she was robbing her body of important nutrients.

Many people in similar situations suffer in silence the pain of gorging followed by vomiting or purging themselves with laxatives. In extreme cases the practice can lead to loss of hair, heart ailments, or kidney diseases, and even death. Ignorant of the possible side effects of bulimia, many suffer in solitude because they are ashamed of the practice. It is estimated that perhaps one million or more young people are in the grip of bulimia as a defense against obesity.

Annette had been somewhat stabilized by the dangerous practice, but not sufficiently to catch up on her studies before the school year ended. Arriving home, she found her mother caught up in a whirl of agents and fellow entertainers preparing for a European tour. In haste, her mother looked at Annette, saying, "What happened to you? You look like something the cat dragged in."

"Thanks for the tender welcome," Annette retorted, deeply disappointed because she had in past weeks determined to get along better with her mother.

The woman tossed a perfunctory kiss as she followed the handyman loaded with suitcases. Annette had no opportunity for a heart-to-heart talk with her mother. "Elizabeth, the new housekeeper, will look after you," the woman said. Yes, Annette thought, there were so many gowns to try on, to shop for, and the hustle and bustle. That was her mother. "Well," her mother flung at her, "I guess you're finished with college—your marks! My God, you're not much good for anything. Anyway," she added absentmindedly, "I can't think now. Enjoy yourself; I'll write when I get to London—but don't worry, I'll be very busy."

I won't worry, Annette thought bitterly, and retreated to her room. She gazed morosely past the spreading lawns to the fitful waves of Long Island Sound. And again she felt the loneliness and rejection like slowly rising water to drown her.

Depression   Before many weeks had passed, Annette had taken a complete turn on the Wheel of Despair, had reached the last spoke and plunged into a chronic depression—withdrawn and seemingly little aware of her environment. Elizabeth, the cook and housekeeper, was unconcerned and somewhat glad that her charge gave so little trouble, except that she consumed vast quantities of food at mealtimes. And Annette reenforced her compulsion by repeated gorging in the privacy of her bedroom.

Bloated of body, puffy of face, ravenous in appetite, the girl sat, her features unchanging and rigid. Gazing into space, she seemed like an automaton without power or direction, headed nowhere. A doctor was called and prescribed a variety of pills, tranquilizers counterbalanced with stimulants. Elizabeth, as baffled as the physician, tried to reach Annette's mother without success. Finally in desperation she called the father, although she had been ordered not to do so under any circumstances.

Annette could not break through the void that had enveloped her. Somehow she was in a sort of numbness; time had stood still. The nervous breakdown was like a fog through which she had no desire to penetrate. Like a ghost, she floated resignedly without care or emotion.

Somewhere in that emptiness, she felt a hand on her cheek caressing with a slight tremor. The voice that accompanied the touch seemed to come from a great distance. "Annette—dear Annette, what have they done to you?"

Her stare gradually focused, but she still held the stupor as if it were something precious that must be retained against further hurt.

"Annette—speak to me; I'm your father."

It was a dream, she told herself, a cruel fantasy to bring a greater blow. Slowly she detached her father's hand from her cheek, and abruptly turned her head away.

He dropped to his knees to place his arms about her waist, saying, "I've come to get you—to take you home with me. Talk to me, Annette—you're my little girl."

Now she looked down to his face, seeking some evidence of reality. Gradually a transformation came to her features. "Dad—Dad, it's really you."

For two weeks he remained with her. Life returned to her as if she were awakening from a bad dream—and they talked. Finally her eyes flared angrily. "Why," she said, "why did you leave me? All those years and I never saw you; only the letters, and they told me nothing."

"I can understand your bitterness. But now you must

know something, even though it makes me look bad." He stopped, hesitated. "I was not a very good man at the time of the divorce. My record was tarnished. The court decided that I was not a worthy father and denied me even visitation privileges; in fact, I was warned not to see you. A poor influence, the judge decreed, and I suppose he was right. All I know now is that I've missed you terribly all these years. Perhaps I'm unworthy of you even today—but I've always loved you, and I can only hope for your forgiveness."

Tears came to her eyes. Everything he said seemed irrelevant except the sentence, "I've always loved you." Finally, she asked, "You really will take me away—and never let me see this house again?"

"You're twenty-one now. You're a woman, and no one has a right to tell you what to do."

"And mother," she muttered sharply. "I'm really free," she added, with a smile of peace and sudden wonder at the realization. That night, alone in her room, she sang all the old songs that she had almost forgotten.

Years later, the public never knew of Annette's past. She sang with extraordinary feeling—now a professional singer whose melodies reflected sadness and gladness intermingled. The Songbird of the Sun, one critic called her, while another wrote that her songs embodied the endless and universal struggle of the human race and its ultimate triumph.

Annette, now a woman, voluptuous and shapely in figure, could smile as if embracing her audiences. She at last had no further compulsion to fight anxiety because her main frustration had been removed when she obtained the love and affection that for so long she had missed and desired. She had no more need of obesity and uncontrolled eating as a futile attempt to escape frustration.

Review of the Process

First we noted that Annette's frustrations were most evident in her chronic feelings about family discord and lack of love. This was followed by anxiety, succeeded by anger as a defense against the anxiety. Her next reaction was guilt, which in turn caused self-hate, and that defense led to depression. The progression was like the cycle of spokes on a wheel, each advance to undo the previous emotional state. The wheel made a complete rotation, which in Annette's case led to a nervous breakdown.

Not all frustrations, of course, result in such a serious outcome. The frustrations that are linked to overweight, while not always so severe, nevertheless are generally accompanied by anxiety. And each mind-set can move the wheel on to the next cycle, which is always worse than the previous one.

The victim of heavy frustrations does not necessarily go through the whole gamut of sequences of the symbolic wheel. Depending not only on circumstances, but also on the basic personality, one may become fixated at a particular spot or spoke, going neither up nor down in the cycle. For example, a person may react with intense anger without feeling the subsequent guilt that attacks a more sensitive person. The psychopath, for instance, will kill without the least remorse.

There are three main types of personality, each possessing a predominant trait. One personality is unduly aggressive, another has a tendency to run away from problems, and a third has no inclination either to fight or to escape, submitting, yielding to inertia, doing nothing about frustration or anxiety.

The person with a serious obesity problem who is overaggressive will generally fight—even though it be self-defeating—trying to handle anxiety by experiencing anger, guilt, self-hate, and finally depression. You will recall how Annette continued her fight through various means, even bulimia, until she finally broke down. Such a person is like a man in combat who continues to fight although he is struck down repeatedly and defeated at every turn.

On the other hand, the person with a tendency to run away denies that he is in the midst of a battle, as if the problem of overweight did not exist. He is aware of his obesity, but he will rationalize its inevitability. Such a person, for example, blames his obesity on inherent characteristics, body build, or genetic factors.

The third type, the submissive person, gives up. He decides that nothing can be done about his obesity. Among the lower animals, a creature sometimes "plays dead," turning on its back and exposing the vulnerable throat area to the enemy as if saying: "Do what you will, I won't resist, I am at your mercy." That is often the way of the submissive person who accepts overweight as a fate that he must bear, a sort of dilemma for which he accepts responsibility, but to which he submits. He will live with the anxiety, anger, and disappointment and not lift a finger to remedy his condition. He does not fight, nor does he seek to run away from his discomfort, but accepts it because he has little motivation for making any changes.

However, the predominant tendency among obese people is to run away from the problem. For example, Americans spend over half a million dollars a year merely to put themselves to sleep, to dull the mind in order to ease the sickness within. More than 800,000 pounds of barbiturates are produced each year, available to the many who long for a rest from conflict and disappointment. At least temporary oblivion is granted to the weary traveler. His nerves and emotions are left to the silent subconscious, though even dreams are denied from that part of his mind. The next morning, however, or after the indulgence, he slowly gropes his way back to reality, still in something of a stupor like a drunk after an alcoholic binge. Some two hundred other sleeping potions are easily obtained by the person who wants escape in numbness.

Possibly even more dangerous are the people under the influence of a variety of drugs—antihistamines, tranquilizers, antispasmodics, amphetamines, and others.

The user of LSD can have more harrying reactions. The temporary glory of the passing scene, the complete surrender to the vivid images drawn from the depth of himself, sometimes give way to sights and sounds infinitely worse than those he wished to avoid. The heroin addict, too, is grateful for the stupor that descends upon him, giving no thought to the pitiful figure of a teenager sprawled, limbs awry, dead of an overdose in a dingy hallway.

The person with serious conflicts and possibly with a weight problem who fails to confront his frustrations feels his days to be empty, without meaning or happiness. He will respond to a mood elevator—a temporary lift—but he will require progressively more drugs to enslave him as the price of escape.

Drugs are prescribed by many physicians for weight control. They include barbiturates, amphetamines, laxatives, diuretics, thyroid extract, and digitalis. None of these in small quantities work in reducing weight. If taken in larger doses, however, they do serve the purpose at the risk of serious side effects and they are certainly dangerous according to medical authorities.

Scandalous and sad as it is that such drugs are prescribed, people still take this useless and potentially tragic route in their attempts to rid themselves of fat. It is estimated that 5,000 to 7,000 unscrupulous physicians gross a billion dollars a year from prescribing two billion diet pills to some ten million deceived people. Weight control prescriptions are scattered indiscriminately by physicians who seem more interested in fees than in the welfare of their patients. The danger, of course, lies in side effects, including drug addiction and even death. The amphetamines intended to be an appetite suppressant, for example, can often become a compulsion until they are more harmful than the obesity.

It has been estimated that about 75 percent of all accidents are caused by angry and emotionally disturbed people. The frustrations, for example, associated with the onset of adulthood between the ages of sixteen and twenty-four account for the greatest number of accidents among these young people.

Sex crime is generally due to a desire for violence rather than for sexual satisfaction. Certainly mutilation of a victim is utterly sadistic. But while the anxiety may have arisen from sexual frustration in cases of rape, the blocking of completely unrelated needs may be the motive providing the impetus to the act.

The self-hate spoke on the Wheel of Despair is tragically illustrated in psychosomatic illnesses that may have some similarity to obesity. Psychosomatic symptoms appear in a variety of physical dysfunctions or specific illnesses such as psoriasis, some forms of arthritis, and many other disabilities that are at least partially caused by emotional and stressful situations. Often repressed hate is the villain; the victim is generally afflicted with latent rage for which there is no outside outlet. It is necessarily turned against himself in the form of psychosomatic disorders.

An illness that is perhaps allied is anorexia nervosa. Like bulimia, the disorder typically afflicts young women of comparatively affluent families. Victims of anorexia nervosa are often attractive before the disease takes hold. They tend to be high achievers who make unusual demands on themselves and have an overwhelming desire to be thin. This compulsion leads to an aversion to food.

The methods used are similar to those employed by victims of bulimia; however, it is easy to distinguish between the two types. The victims of bulimia, for example, manage to retain a normal appearance, but the anorectics stand out because of their shrunken bodies. They are perfectionists, so intent on their desire to be thin that they view their emaciated appearance as a reward for their success in eliminating flesh.

Anorexia nervosa often has its onset after a social trauma: a broken romance or engagement, a divorce or separation, the loss of a loved one. The previous obsession with food is replaced by a revulsion against it as the victim's life falls apart and it becomes impossible to form close relationships with friends or lovers.

Anorexia nervosa is little understood by modern science, but the self-starvation of comparatively affluent young females has been known as a clinical entity since 1694, when it was described by a physician known as Morton. Since that time the disease has been recognized in a variety of theoretical models, medical, behavioral, and psychoanalytic, but the mortality rate continues at 7 to 15 percent of cases. Although meager medical progress has been made for this affliction, the physical criteria for identifying it are well known. The anorectic loses weight to a serious degree, accompanied by amenorrhea, a distortion of body image, and social restriction.

It has been recently pointed out that the disorder is linked to psychological factors, particularly those involved in relationships existing in the home.

The most famous example of anorexia nervosa is that of

Elizabeth Barrett, who became the wife of the famous poet Robert Browning. Her case is historic, having been studied widely by the medical profession and clinical psychologists. Psychoanalysts have given their interpretations, and at the other extreme Elizabeth's fate has been ascribed to demons who decreed a living death and to divine punishment for sins not acknowledged but demanding penance. Despite the varied theories, we can still affirm that the basic factor involved unmet needs and frustrated desires, creating an anxiety that took her to the cycle of self-hate as a defense.

Elizabeth was the daughter of Edward Barrett, whose wealth accrued from slave holdings in Jamaica. She was brought up pampered and well supplied for physical needs and surrounded by overprotection. In her thirteenth year, she was already described as beautiful, almost astral in spirit. Unfortunately, her psychological needs were far from being met.

At fifteen, she became ill, afflicted with anorexia nervosa. Nevertheless her renown as an author grew. The public was fascinated by the mystery of this strange girl, by her genius and brilliance. At the age of thirty-eight she had become a legend, but she weighed a mere eighty-eight pounds.

After her marriage to Browning, her health improved. She saw the vivid contrast between her own family and that of her husband, whose home radiated love and happy relationships. She could see her father's many idiosyncrasies, keeping the family submissive in the coldness of the atmosphere in which she had grown up.

Her father had held himself strictly aloof, rigid, keeping the family always under his control, allowing no self-responsibility. The smallest deviation was swiftly condemned, and the family was locked away from the outside world. Consequently, Elizabeth had had no chance to grow, to find self-identity. Her father was in command, enforcing his rules ruthlessly.

Her father never forgave her for leaving his domain. He wrote only once, and that was to denounce and disown her. As far as he was concerned, she was dead.

Although she never attained robust health, still her new life was full of love, and she expressed her gratitude in a few lines to her husband:

> I yield the grave for thy sake, and exchange
> My near view of Heaven for earth with thee.

Elizabeth had found happiness, a return to well-being, by removing her main frustation, that of unmet need for honest affection. Browning wrote no poem more beautiful than his act of bestowing love and life on a woman rescued from hell into the heaven of self-fulfillment.

Another example of uncontrolled weight, which turned out less happily than that of Elizabeth, concerns a celebrity of more recent years—the tragedy of Judy Garland.

Judy grew up in the "roaring twenties." Bootleg booze and prohibition existed side by side. Charles Lindbergh won $25,000 as a prize for his nonstop flight across the Atlantic Ocean in 1927. Babe Ruth hit 60 home runs that year—and Judy was singing "Bye, Bye Blackbird" and "My Blue Heaven," well on her way to stardom.

But the heartaches in her background were unknown to her adoring audiences. Speaking of her childhood, she said, "They used to starve me whenever they thought I was putting on weight." Later the efforts to control her appetite included amphetamines and barbiturates. But the day came when she was grossly overweight—one hundred sixty pounds on a frame a little over five feet tall. Her body was bloated, her face puffy, her ankles thick and swollen. She suffered from depression and was afraid of the dark, afraid of sleep—afraid of death. She had a phobic fear of flying and endured torture in flight.

What were the frustrations that made her life a continuous tug-of-war with her weight? Most of the events of her career can be identified on the Wheel of Despair, pegged on the emotional cycles already described.

Her childhood was a nightmare from which she never recovered. Perhaps no woman had been so subjected to emotional shocks in spite of her worldwide successes. Judy was bullied by her mother, her producers, her husbands, and a myriad agents and business associates.

She came from a broken home, from discord and the insecurity of divided loyalty, one parent against the other. She wanted love and affection above all else, and even when the world acclaimed her the greatest singer of popular songs, she could not find the love that her psyche had missed so much in childhood.

Upon her death at the age of forty-seven in 1969, she had succumbed to anorexia nervosa, a gaunt little woman in the merry-go-round of her weight problem. Even though her name was fixed in the hearts of millions, she had never conquered herself and the tragedy of her unmet need for simple and sincere love.

PART TWO

The Solution

Cast thy bread upon the waters:
for thou shalt find it after many days.

—Ecclesiastes 10:20

Chapter **V**

Forethoughts

It has been established that frustrations induce anxiety, which subsequently impels a person to seek various means to escape that anxiety. This process frequently leads to the problem of overweight, one of the self-defeating behavioral responses. The fat person could have chosen a number of other neurotic courses of action instead of obesity. But apparently you made your decision, consciously or subconsciously, to become fat, and now you yearn to do something about it.

"All right," you may say, "I agree with some of the things that you stress. But I want to know specifically what I can do about my problem. I've tried diets, exercise, and who knows what else. Nothing works for any length of time. Now you're asking me to believe in something new. Quite frankly," you may add, "I'm a little confused by the psychological mumbo-jumbo. Tell me what to do. Why don't you explain to me in one sentence what it's all about?"

Okay, here it is: *You are fat because you're frustrated.*

Is that clear enough?

Once you have accepted that fact, the next step is to get rid of the frustrations that have led you indirectly to your present dilemma.

Now you say, "Well, how do I succeed in doing that?"

So, here is your answer: *You remove frustrations by getting what you desire.* "Great," you counter, "I want the Brooklyn Bridge." And then you grow more serious, "I really would like to kick my brother-in-law. By your reasoning all I have to do to control my weight is to put an ax to his head."

Now our whole argument seems to fall apart. People steal one another's wives, bank clerks filch some of the money that they handle, muggers trample on old ladies, priests have secret and guilty thoughts about voluptuous parishioners, and national leaders desire the death of their enemies. They are all frustrated—and at fault in seeking illegally to remove the frustrations.

And here you may interrupt, saying, "And you tell me that I am fat because I'm frustrated—unable to get what I desire."

But would it make you happy to kill your brother-in-law because you desire to do so? Do you really want to mug an old lady? And the money you might steal from the bank would soon evaporate—and you wouldn't like the jail term. Finally, it is questionable that the man of the cloth could enjoy a sexual escapade without consequences. Of course, antisocial acts do occur frequently in our culture. But the desire to slash a victim for a gold chain or a few dollars is often a screen for a deeper unmet need in the criminal's life.

Regardless of subconscious motives, obviously we must define the sort of frustrations that are the root cause of difficulties. The wife stealer, for example, may not have a sexual problem, but rather one of communication and lack of a sense of self-worth. The bank clerk may have a greater need of a sense of achievement and recognition. The mugger, or even the drug addict, may really desire a sense of belonging and self-respect.

It is apparent that we often do not know what we really desire, and thus it is difficult to pinpoint the frustrations that engender anxiety and self-defeating behavior.

Finally, exasperated, you may say, "Well, I am not a victim of bulimia or anorexia nervosa. I merely want a more presentable waistline. If not all frustrations are applicable, then tell me exactly what kind you are talking about."

The frustrations in question come from denial of wants that are universal and basic to our psychological peace of mind. These include a sense of belonging, a need to achieve, love and affection, sex, freedom from fear, freedom from guilt, and a need for sharing, understanding, and self-respect. If these needs are fulfilled, the unacceptable desires will disappear. Without frustration of these basic desires, there will be no chronic frustrations—and perhaps more important to you, the excess poundage will no longer be required as a defense against anxiety.

The point has been made that obesity is generally a mild form of neurosis. Second, it has been proved by much research that a neurosis is always caused by frustrations, conscious or unconscious, by unmet needs. The solution seems obvious. We must satisfy the universal needs listed above. The frustrations are thus eliminated, no longer identified with anxiety. The overweight that was a defense against the twin factors of frustration and anxiety no longer has a reason for existence. The compulsive overeating disappears as a result of the new peace of mind and improved psychological health.

Do you really want to lose weight?

The answer is a resounding yes. But you must be prepared for a few surprises under the system recommended here. First, you must drop any diet or regime with which you may have been struggling.

Forget about losing weight   Astonishing as this instruction may be, yet it must be emphasized.

There is a course of action necessary before you can be successful at weight control. A tumor must be removed before good health can be restored. Your psychological needs must be satisfied before you can lose weight permanently without hassle, torment, and repeated failure.

You should not seek directly to get rid of your excess weight. There is a better and workable way to accomplish this task. First, you must remove the causes, the psychological factors behind the compulsive eating.

Don't worry about your weight for now. Your attention to excess poundage will come later. Once your psychological needs are met and satisfied, you will find the attainment of the desired figure easy without tremendous efforts of will or suffering.

After we have stressed that you will not permanently resolve your weight problem unless you meet your psychological needs, the next principle may seem paradoxical. Your needs will not be realized only by your own will power or direct aim. The second rule is therefore as follows:

Use reciprocal tactics   Get your needs satisfied indirectly through others. This principle has been enunciated in a number of books of the type, "How to Make Friends and Influence People." In our method it requires first meeting the needs of others, with the consequence that it accomplishes three purposes: 1) the obese person is distracted from awareness of his discomfort; 2) in meeting someone else's psychological needs, the obese person gains a vicarious sense of meeting his own; and 3) goodwill and a debt to be repaid in kind are created on the part of the other person, thus providing the reciprocal conditions for the obese person to meet his own needs.

The first principle, that of temporarily putting aside attempts to lose weight, leaves the person free to concentrate on the primary cause of his trouble. The second principle, that of reciprocal maneuvers, uses the age-old and proven tactic of obtaining one's wants through others. After all, how can any self-realization and happiness be obtained except through communication? Self-fulfillment is never achieved in a vacuum. A person cannot shut himself in his room to await happiness. One tends to lose identity unless acknowledged by others. An artist can paint a work of genius, but it seems not to exist until people admire it. How happy is the previously obese person when she finds others admiring her for a beautiful figure.

To appreciate and fully understand the course of action herein recommended, one must follow the step-by-step procedures described in the chapters to come.

You want a slim figure, and complementarily better mental health. Our aim is for the first; the second is a by-product, an extra dividend.

Chapter *VI*

Belonging

Every person needs companionship, the reassurance and emotional security that come from belonging to a social unit whose members share the same need.

This psychological want for belonging exists on all socioeconomic levels and in every culture. It may be based partly on the ancient biological struggle for survival. Perhaps primitive man realized that he became better able to provide for his family if he joined other hunters. When enemies threatened, neighbors banded together to repel or to conquer the invaders.

You, too, have that need for belonging, and the likelihood—if you are overweight—is that you have been somehow denied that need, that your circle of friends is limited, that you often feel alone, detached from people and without interpersonal relationships. Your frustration involves being deprived of a sense of belonging, feeling unworthy and unimportant in the eyes of others. As a result you are beset by a sense of alienation. You have sought to defend yourself against the accompanying anxiety by putting on weight, as if you wished to console yourself for the hurt by pampering your body.

Things to Do

The miracle is that you exist as a unique individual different from all others, one among countless millions. You meet or come in contact with someone else who likewise is unique. Somehow out of ages past, both of you are on the same stage, loving, struggling, and living often in loneliness.

You and that other person move on the same earth, in the same country, village, or town. In spite of differences, you have a need in common, that of being linked through a feeling of belonging. You cannot get that need satisfied without another person. Only a human being can grant that gift to others. Accordingly, you can become an ambassador of goodwill, purveying a sense of belonging to your associates.

And now you have the secret. You will acquire a sense of belonging for yourself by giving that feeling to others. Like the biblical promise, your bread is cast upon the waters, later to return to you as your reward.

You must begin your campaign to lose weight by forgetting about your goal. You will even forget that you desire to gain your own sense of belonging. You will be too busy with an absorbing task, engaged in activities that may prove to be the most important in your life.

At this point, you have only one aim, and that is the engendering of a sense of belonging in others.

Start your campaign by deciding to encourage a feeling of belonging in anyone with whom you come in contact. Determine to keep the goal in mind in all your social and business relationships. This involves many little acts and seemingly insignificant gestures. You will look for ways to make others feel good about themselves. Perhaps you will tell little white lies such as, "You look so well today." That person will feel better, and although your comment may be far from the truth, it is no lie that someone who is in a bad mood can be perked up by a simple remark that tends to elevate his or her self-esteem.

Remember at this point that you are doing things not for your benefit, but for another person. In order to get the reciprocity in motion, you must forget about yourself, in other words, indirectly sidetracking your own anxiety by working for others. Later you will see that such temporary unselfishness will redound to your advantage.

Be cheerful as much as possible even if it hurts. Your own moods are directly and subtly conveyed to people around you. Remoteness, detachment, and a "touch me not" attitude cast a pall on human relationships. And shyness is a fear of rejection and abandonment, assuring that you will be shunned if you persist in the fear. Dare to take chances of rebuff and misunderstanding by some people. Smile and go on with your campaign of openness and positive attitudes in spite of disappointments. There are too many people out there who hunger for a sense of belonging. Give it to them. Later a magic fulfillment will become evident in your own person, but that element of self-reward must be postponed.

So, on this day, you determine to be cheerful, to spread joy instead of gloom. This admonishment is as old as the wisdom of the human race. It remains a constructive device to lighten the burden of others. Ingrain it in your conscious mind until it becomes a habit that sinks deep into your subconscious as an automatic response in your dealings with others.

Every time you feel impelled to make a nasty remark, replace it with an opposite comment that is constructive and ego-lifting instead of destructive. Everybody has good and evil within him. It is just as easy to see the healthy and the wholesome part of a person as it is to note the undesirable.

If rebuffed, turn away without recrimination or scar. You value your power for good too much to repay in kind.

Incidentally, one who flings discourtesies and bitter words is accustomed to expect a similar backlash from those he abuses. A calm and unreproachful attitude, perhaps an expression of sympathy for the person's problem, sets him back in amazement. And in the subsequent silence may lie some regret for the rudeness—thereby instilling a marginal sense of belonging in the poor soul.

A woman was having her car tuned up, and she needed transportion the next day. "Can I get my car tomorrow morning?" she asked.

"Lady, I'm no magician," the grizzled mechanic growled. "There are other cars ahead of you. You dames expect . . ."

"Excuse me," the woman cut in, smiling. "I know how busy you are—how can you remember all the parts of a car? That's more learning than a college education. Really, I admire what you do."

The man hesitated, puzzled and undecided, accustomed to arguments and accusations.

"But, anyway," the woman continued, "I know you'll do the best you can."

"Huh," the man said.

"You're very kind." She started to walk away.

"Lady—wait a minute." He rubbed the palm of a hand against his pants leg. "I'll have your car ready at nine o'clock tomorrow morning."

"Oh, thank you—you're indeed kind."

A companion turned to her as they left the garage. "Gosh," she said. "How in the world did you do that—that mechanic looks meaner than a bear."

"No problem," the woman replied smugly. "You know the old saying about using honey to catch flies."

Have you ever been invited to the home of an acquaintance where you were received politely enough? Everything seemed in order, the rooms were graciously adorned. The greetings were correct, but guarded in manner. You were offered refreshments. But somehow there was something lacking as the conversation flowed. You did not feel at home. There was an indefinite aura that somehow left you cold, an undercurrent of uneasiness.

A visit to another home was so much more pleasant. Perhaps it was not so well appointed, perhaps somewhat in disorder. And yet the greetings reached out with warmth although the words may have been the same. You felt really wanted because of an intangible sense of belonging in that home. There was no special effort at communication, merely a flowing of friendliness and acceptance. Your own importance, social position, or even the purpose of your visit were overlooked. There was just a feeling of genuine sincerity in the gladness to see you.

What a difference between the two homes, a difference that on the surface seemed irrelevant, but was so real that the two actually existed worlds apart.

Your home, whether it be a spacious house or a one-room apartment, can reflect a sense of belonging for those who pass your threshold. It can be a refuge in a turbulent world, where easy laughter and a positive atmosphere exist, radiating seemingly from the very walls because the inhabitant vibrates with goodwill. Hominess is inherent in that sincerity. People no longer feel alienated, no longer strangers in your home. You are a vibrant, living person who somehow conveys a feeling of belonging to everyone who enters your home.

The magic of touch is obvious to everyone. There are some people, however, who recoil from the touch of another person. That characteristic is sick, a reaction formation because of prior disappointments, perhaps buried fears of being rejected. It is a defense against further possible hurt from risking emotional contact with someone who might ultimately turn away.

Most people, however, react favorably to the human touch. This form of satisfaction is based on the infant's original and vital need to feel the mother's breast, the touch of her loving hand. That need remains with us as long as we live. And you, aware of this universal desire, can use it again and again in your campaign to bestow a sense of belonging.

Some sociologists have given the practice of shaking hands a pragmatism that it does not deserve. It was, they argue, a means of self-defense when two warriors met, extending a hand to show that it held no weapon. Some psychologists, on the other hand, perceive a more humane purpose in the custom. You shake hands as a means of establishing contact through touch, affirming friendship and a feeling of belonging in each other's sphere of existence.

Strange as it may seem, the custom of driving on the right side of the road is directly linked to the desire to belong, to feel accepted, and to convey a similar feeling to another person. With the vast expanse of land and the meager population in our early history, in the loneliness and isolation there was a great need for human contact. Meeting another wagon on the trail, each driver felt the need to stop. As the two travelers stepped down from their wagons, their horses had to be held with strong right hands. Accordingly, each team was on the right side of its driver, leaving both men free to face each other and converse safely as long as they wished.

We therefore drive on the right side of the road in this country because people were eager to talk to one another. Two men talked on a lonely trail, perhaps touched hands, and for moments realized the joy of even a brief and passing friendship.

When you shake hands, make it a meaningful social gesture. If your hand is limp and lifeless, it indicates that you do not care. But if your hand is too strong, it conveys an aggressive, dominating personality. Put feeling in your hand, confident but gentle. You are actually uniting your body with someone else's.

Touching is a means of saying that the other person belongs in your world. Touch the free arm lightly if you wish to emphasize the fact that you like that person. Belonging is partly in your hands. The magic touch is yours to mold and to bring much to others who yearn for closer human relationships.

There are many little things you can do to spread the spirit of belonging. If you have your goal clearly in mind, you will find many other gracious gestures at your disposal.

If you have not seen someone for a while, for example, you may call and say, "I'm sorry I haven't seen you recently. I hope you are well and still your cheerful self." Send "get well" cards when it is appropriate and holiday cards, not merely trusting to the printed messages, but personalizing them with your own words.

When you meet a friend or acquaintance, you might say, "I've missed you," and otherwise indicate that he or she is needed and appreciated.

If you must criticize, blame the specific wrong rather than a given person. Comment favorably about other people. Let others be bitter; you haven't time for the negative. Express approval of a color scheme, a new dress or suit, an attractive necktie or scarf, a new hairdo.

Give the person the feeling that he is accepted even though you may not really approve of certain behavior. Make it clear that individuality can be desirable. Be outwardly nonjudgmental. Perhaps the very sense of belonging that you project could result in making the person more conscious of his idiosyncrasies.

Show that you are interested in other people. Ask them about their activities, ambitions, and goals in life. Listening can be effective in making others feel important, enhancing their feeling of self-worth. Pay particular attention to those who are usually neglected and submissive as well as those who are overaggressive. Both have a burning desire to be recognized and appreciated.

Arrange for a person who doesn't belong to show special skills before a group—play an instrument, tell a story, or show pictures of travels or a hobby.

You can lend your home for informal get-togethers in a welcoming atmosphere—small parties, committee work, discussion of community affairs, and good fellowship.

These are mere suggestions; there are many ways of engendering a sense of belonging. Knowing the objective of your campaign, you will think of numerous other appropriate devices.

And the aim of all this suddenly comes to light. By instilling a sense of belonging in others, almost miraculously you have acquired it for yourself. In the process of helping others, you have absorbed that important need yourself. At last you feel recognized, admired, and a vital part of your world. People tend to respond in a similar manner; those who shunned you in the past now seek you out. But entirely apart from the actions of others, you have gained within yourself that precious gift of belonging. Your own need has been fulfilled. Ultimately this must change your attitudes and personality. Thus as our plan develops—with possible omissions or alterations—you become more capable of handling any neurotically tinged problems that you may have had, including that of being unable to control your weight. In other words, by gaining a feeling of belonging as you helped to bestow it on others, you have already started to remove one of your own frustrations, thus reducing the compulsive urge to overeat.

Chapter VII

Achievement

Now that you have acknowledged your need for belonging as vital to your psychological health, you are ready to tackle another need; namely, that of achievement. You will proceed in the same manner, helping others to meet this need in their personal lives. Indirectly you will thus satisfy your own. In this process, it will become evident that your anxiety is lessened. Subsequently, the tension that previously impelled you to intemperance in eating will be less urgent or compelling.

Achievement is necessary for survival. With our first breath we seek to overcome obstacles to nourishment and warmth. This drive is one of our first psychological needs.

If for a moment the body ceased to do the work of circulation and metabolism, the person would quickly be dead. If we stopped struggling for a livelihood or lessened the fight against the environment, molding it and resisting it to gain what is essential for existence and well-being, man would certainly sink back into inertia and death. Achievement is essential for biological reasons. The same drive to achieve is further vital to psychological health. A person's worth is largely judged by his ability to function, to achieve; and his self-esteem is directly linked to this sense of achievement.

Such an intrinsic need therefore deserves your attention and determination, to further the development of a healthy sense of achievement in others. There are varied ways in which this can be accomplished. The goal is to engender a perception of achievement in those with whom you come in contact.

If you are a working person, your fellow employees and your superiors are the proper objects of your campaign to spread this sense of achievement. Cheerfulness and the devices described in the previous chapter are suitable here as well; but our aim is to enhance a feeling of achievement primarily. Of course, the improvement of your own personality as a result of the acquisition of an awareness of belonging is a definite advantage in this task.

You know that high morale is of first importance in any business, service, or industrial establishment. A constructive atmosphere is engendered by making others feel good about themselves, by friendliness, cooperation in the conviction that something is being done to convey the sense of achievement. In our vast mechanical and technological complex, that need is too often lost in impersonal relationships.

Spread the spirit of belonging, offer praise, avoid negative criticism, be an example of a willing and competent worker, clearly getting satisfaction from your job. Remember that fellow workers may have trouble at home, financial problems, family squabbles, and difficulties with neighbors. Be a good listener. Some of these attempts may be misinterpreted as a sort of Uncle Tom complex, but you are concerned with a higher goal; that of meeting the psychological needs of others. Suggestions of an ulterior motive can be overlooked because of the greater advantage to be derived.

An awareness of achievement is imbued not only on the job. That is only one of the many areas where the need can be met. This fact is particularly significant to those unemployed or not yet employed, and particularly to the millions of workers whose jobs are tedious, unrewarding, and monotonous, done merely to earn a living, with no overall satisfaction. In fact, those are the very people who can most use your help in meeting their psychological needs.

It is also possible to inculcate a sense of achievement in a person's social life.

Achievement is a relative term. A person may seek unreasonable success, never reaching perfectionist goals that are in fact unattainable. But achievement is merely the feeling that one has completed something considered satisfactory and rewarding. With most people a series of small accomplishments can meet essential needs. The person does not necessarily expect to become president of the firm where he is employed. He simply wants enough achievement to make him feel good about himself as an average person.

Merely expressing approval in minor matters can raise spirits and give a sense of achievement. For example, when you enter someone's home, look around for something to approve or praise—a picture, the decor, the host's appearance. Just a passing remark may change a visit into a really pleasant encounter, conveying a feeling that the other persons have accomplished something worthwhile in their environment.

At a social gathering, your aim should be to make someone feel accepted and interesting. A young girl, Mary, was going to her first senior prom, a date that she had been proud to accept because her escort was a handsome man, popular and sought after on the campus. But as the days passed before the affair, she became nervous, possessed by self-doubt. Often she seemed to have spoiled evenings with other dates because of her shyness and feelings of unworthiness. Her insecurity paradoxically was seen as aloofness and indifference, and consequently her social life had indeed been dull and indifferent.

As the fateful evening drew nigh, more and more her anxiety increased. Why had he chosen her? There were many pretty girls, any one of whom would be more cheerful and charming. She prepared herself for disaster. She was just too gauche, she reasoned. How about her dress? What would she talk about? She visualized herself rejected during the evening, winding up alone while her date danced with others. Finally in her sad expectations she was on the verge of canceling the date.

Highly agitated, she sat across my desk in the office, speaking in a low tone. "It's not only my fear of this fellow," she said. "I've been hoping for a date with him for so long. It's that I feel no good, a dud. I can't do anything right."

Poor Mary, she had been too preoccupied with herself to realize that self-fulfillment can be realized only through others.

Her immediate dilemma with her important date was solved by asking her to follow a simple formula, in fact, to play a game. She was instructed to think solely of her escort and his feelings, to encourage him to talk about himself, comment on his dancing, his appearance, and anything that would make him feel a sense of worth and achievement.

Her immediate reaction to my recommendations was that I was asking her to give up her own individuality and independence.

"Wait a minute," I said. "How have you managed to possess a sense of self-worth in the past?"

"Well, I'm pretty independent . . . ." she started to say.

"Pardon me for interrupting," I put in, "but are you happy?"

"No," she said, lowering her head.

Days later, her mother reported that Mary was delighted with the senior prom. Once she had made her companion feel comfortable with her, she dared to forget about the game as both enjoyed themselves. She had indeed not given up her independence, nor had she been subservient. She had merely assured a sense of achievement in her escort, while becoming relaxed herself in the process because she was no longer thinking solely of her own person. As a consequence, not only was she relieved of anxiety, but she came across as the charming person she really was.

Another method of inculcating a sense of achievement is to help someone overcome a bad habit. For example, if you want to help another person to give up smoking, you can agree on a pact that neither of you will indulge in the habit. The other person's morale and determination to abstain are firmed up by the knowledge that he has support and an ally in his efforts.

Organizations such as Alcoholics Anonymous, SmokeEnders, Weight Watchers, and others gain their strength from that cooperative and supporting role that has an element of benign big brother or father watching over them, with the sense of achievement resulting.

The popular group therapy also derives its efficacy from the sense of belonging engendered by the group in addition to the feeling of achievement gained from greater self-understanding.

Ways of bestowing on others a sense of achievement are numerous. If you have firmly in mind the desire to help others reach this goal, countless opportunities will arise.

You will recognize that the devices are repeatedly used

in business. The salesman's effectiveness is often based on his ability to establish a bridge to his customer by showing a personal interest, by personal touches to convey that the potential customer will derive satisfaction from the product.

Sports have that strong element of playing the game, the intensification of expression. On the handball or tennis court, the golf links, or whatever your game, be aware of the other's need to get a sense of achievement. Never belittle your opponent's play. Good sportsmanship, praise, courtesy, and consideration for the other person's pride and dignity are all elements that make a competitor feel good, win or lose.

If you have a hobby, try to get someone else involved so that he also can reap pleasure from it. Stamp or coin collecting, for example, can enlarge a person's horizon, providing a sense of achievement—particularly if done with someone whose enthusiasm is catching.

Everywhere you go in personal contacts, by telephone or correspondence, openings occur for emphasizing a sense of achievement in others. The stage is set for you in fraternal organizations, political and school activities, churches, community, and last, but not least, within the family itself.

And, again, as you work on the sense of belonging, you automatically satisfy that need for yourself. In making others feel that they are successful in achieving, you amazingly realize a sense of achievement in your own being. People are more drawn to you because you seem always to make them increasingly at peace with themselves.

You have actually performed a double service, one for others and even more important, one for yourself. Each need that you satisfy builds up like an ever-mounting pyramid, the foundation more firmly in place, until you reach a level of emotional maturity and peace within yourself.

The consequence is the lessening in the depths of your own psyche of another segment of frustration, part of which was the cause of your compulsion to eat more than required for a healthy body.

Chapter **VIII**

Fear

Everybody is afraid of something, whether consciously or subconsciously, ranging from a mild fear of slipping on an icy sidewalk to the overwhelming fear of the phobias. As with anxiety, which is quite similar, there are various types of fears. You are afraid of things outside yourself based on reality. Who is not afraid of nuclear war, even of crime in our cities?

We are all afraid of extreme frustrations that may threaten our peace of mind and even our survival. Little wonder that fears can create the anxiety that some people seek to avoid by eating too much, withdrawing into the self-centeredness of pampering themselves with food as a defense against a threatening world.

Many people also fear their own aggressive drive, afraid that in anger they might inflict real harm on someone. No one can predict how violent he might become under extremely trying situations. The very person who argues long and passionately against violence may surprise himself at the cruelty he might practice if his own child were attacked, or in times of war and social upheaval.

How many people are afraid of their sexual drive, fearing what they might do if they actualized their fantasies?

If we could see clearly the evil residing in each and every one of us, we might recoil in horror. Generally we allow subconscious urges to penetrate our consciousness only in dreams, symbolic images fleeting in disguise, peeking only briefly out of fantasies. This is said to be fear of the id, that hidden part of ourselves without morals or conscience.

The price that civilization exacts for its benefits involves bridling the id to make a society safe from the violence of uncontrolled aggression. To achieve that restraint, the authorities have to impose certain rules, in the process creating counterfears. These are the fears of authority figures and the rules that they have imprinted upon our subconscious from a very early age as unchanging moral laws— moral in the eyes of the moralizer. The expected actions and reactions are ingrained in us and influence our lives as though in response to a repetitive computer, printing out the same message for a given period of culture. If we were to count the things forbidden in a given society at some period in its development, we would find that at one time eating tomatoes or using tobacco or even thinking of the opposite sex were stepping-stones on the way to hell.

The response to fear is the same as the reaction to anxiety or any other emotional disturbance. Some people refuse to consider or change the harmful tendencies, resigning themselves to the discomfort of their unending and unchanging fears. The "do-nothing" people are to be pitied, since their fears remain permanent and chronic.

Others run away from their condition. They go to extremes to avoid any link or situation even remotely connected with the feared environmental aspects.

A third type of fear-afflicted people are those who suffer from phobias. Their anxiety leads to a tragic condition that severely limits their activities. They may shun open places, shun certain objects to the extent that they cannot leave the safety of their homes. Fear of conscience, for example, while having some positive aspects, can be an enslaving condition, limiting healthy expression and emotional stability.

Here is an immensely important area in which you can engender happier living by helping others to get rid of useless and impeding fears.

If you are to foster freedom from fear in another person, your task may be simplified by determining the category of his fear. Is it an apprehension based on reality? For example, is he afraid of something outside himself such as the possibility of losing his job? Second, is his fear connected with a bad conscience? Third, does it arise from a deeper neurotic disturbance such as a phobia?

Let us take the case of a man who fears the loss of his job. On the surface, it would seem that his worry is reasonable enough. How then could you help him to gain freedom from that fear? You could join in a mutual examination of his problem, to confront it without panic on his part and enable him to decide what course of action would be best. Is his job in danger because of the increasing mechanization of office practices? Perhaps his firm plans extensive automation. Having ascertained that this was true, you could suggest that he upgrade his knowledge at a community college or by night courses in adult education.

Continuing the analysis of his problem, you might point out, if applicable, that his inadequacy at the office may be due to his own personality shortcomings. In such an instance, you are ready and able to convey to him the techniques that you have learned in the two previous chapters. Inability to project a sense of belonging and achievement, lack of adaptability, inability to get along with others all are primary reasons for discharge of employees.

Pointing out his possible lack of skills, the means of remedying the inadequacy, plus the potential negative fac-

tors may be sufficient to save the man's job—or help him
to secure another more suited to his temperament. In any
case, you will have helped him to free himself from fear
through your sympathy, the analysis of the problem, and
the suggested solution. You have listened while he unbur-
dened himself of anxiety, resulting in encouragement and
possibly a new ordering of his priorities.

Moral fears are generally more complicated, and yet are
easily identified. They are felt as guilt or shame. The person stands accused by his conscience, which was early imposed by parents and other authority figures. It is not so
much that the law forbids an act but that something within
points an accusing finger.

It has been said that any power or institution, particularly the family, that governs a child's life for the first
seven years will for the rest of his life be the controlling
influence on him.

The adult is generally little aware of the origin or source
of his conscience. He does not realize that his reaction to
a given situation is often dictated by a voice within himself
that actually belongs to someone else who firmly set his
response tendencies. That force, deeply submerged in his
unconscious mind, tells him when he should feel guilt and
shame. We are all slaves to conscience in varying de-
grees, governed by outmoded taboos and restrictions. When
conscience operates too severely, it stifles psychological
growth and development.

A certain amount of caution is necessary at this point
lest it appear that we should set aside all aspects of conscience as inevitably harmful. Doubtless the development
of conscience was of primary importance for the progress
of mankind. Otherwise we might still be savages, proclaiming ourselves free of self-responsibility. All the evil
in man would flare up without the controlling influence of

conscience. However, most pangs of conscience are not the result of an antisocial nature. They are frequently unjustified, based on outmoded interpretations of moral codes.

You are concerned for a friend or acquaintance whom you wish to help because his conscience is disturbing his functioning and peace of mind. Now that we have looked briefly at the nature of conscience, you can become an instrument for lessening his unnecessary torments. This is part of your campaign to meet the needs of others. You can convey that the victim need not run away from his conscience, nor accept it as his fate.

It has been noted that the more inhibited a person is, the more he tends to be bothered by his conscience. One would suppose that the person without so-called sins would be less concerned with his conscience; however, it seems that the opposite is true.

Your task in helping a person gain freedom from moral guilt is to lessen his concept of self-blame, to examine with him the unreasonable demands he makes upon himself. If God has created us with weaknesses, He has certainly the expectation that such weaknesses will reveal themselves at times. And a wise God, of course, may not agree with many of the questionable values imposed on trusting people. Many of the sins of yesterday are today's virtues.

Encouraging open-mindedness in people who are plagued by an overstrict conscience is the course that you can follow to lessen their moral fears.

Another category of fear is more neurotic because it is seemingly divorced from the conscience, at least on the conscious level. The phobia is a common example of this fear; it is caused by a conflict that has been repressed, shut out from awareness. The person affected has forgotten the original traumatic responses and replaced them by a phobia, fear of a specific and seemingly harmless thing, emotion, or situation. He does not know why he is afraid of cats, horses, open places, water, enclosures, elevators, or a host of other things.

Of course, psychoanalysts and other practitioners of depth psychotherapy cure phobias by having the victim relive the original trauma, ultimately becoming aware of the fundamental cause of his unreasonable fear.

In your campaign to free another person from a phobia you lack the time and the training to use this method. However, the behavioral method utilized by many psychiatrists is easily followed and workable by anyone with common sense. Furthermore, you do not have to know the cause of the problem.

To illustrate the simplicity of the method, let us consider a person who was afraid of open places. Her fear had grown so severe that she refused to leave her room. The rest of the family attended to all the outside chores. Unable to help her, friends finally shunned her.

Because of the chronic nature of her condition, much time passed before she could become free again. However, the procedures in her case are the same that can be adopted in simpler cases. The method merely utilizes reward and punishment. The punishment, of course, is ever present in the phobia, and you need not worry about that part of the behavioral duad. Getting away from the torment and experiencing freedom is the reward, which is given in small doses. Never should the victim be compelled to tolerate what at a given point he or she seems unable to withstand; the term gradual is very important.

Edith, the patient with whom we are concerned, was first treated in her own apartment. She was asked to close her eyes, relax, and imagine an experience as she held my hand. The fantasy was that of walking in her garden, smelling the fragrance of a warm day, listening to the birds, seeing the flowers, touching their velvet smoothness, biting into a ripe fruit plucked from a tree. The aim was, of course, to engender a feeling of reward for having ventured outdoors even if only in her imagination.

The next step was to open the door, letting her look at the front yard. Still holding my hand, nevertheless she trembled. The process of gradually encouraging her to face the outdoors was increased. With praise, each step provided its own reward. Ultimately her phobic fear grew less and less until one day she could say that she was free at last.

The method is simple to use and can be very effective with anyone having a mild phobia. You merely inure the victim gradually to the feared object or situation as the evolving reward provides further progress.

In addition, in helping others to overcome their fears, you succeed in mastering your own through greater understanding. The easiest and most effective way to learn is to teach others. In making efforts to help your fellow human beings, you give your own needs a boost toward fulfillment.

Once more, by diminishing a source of frustration in others, you have mitigated your own fears through better understanding of yourself, thereby reducing a tendency to overeat as a defense.

Chapter IX

Guilt

The relationship between fear and guilt is very close. However, since guilt is such an overwhelming emotion, it is necessary to delve more deeply in the subject.

Guilt in our culture is inevitably linked to aggression and sex. Both of these are basic drives that cannot be indefinitely denied; either must be sublimated or expressed. However, most of man's progress and civilization emerge from these two powerful forces. They are the basis of love, tenderness, family, children, and the warmth of the human heart. Unfortunately, aggression and sex are also the agents behind destruction, cruelty, wars, and the conflicts that tend to obliterate civilization.

Little wonder that this double-edged sword of aggression and sex gives rise to much guilt. Perhaps love and sexual pleasure are twice valued because their negative expressions are felt so deeply. Aggression and sex are frequently overlaid with guilt, because we so easily slip from love into hatred and from hatred into love.

How can you help someone caught in a web as complicated as that of guilt?

Let's take the experience of a man whose sense of guilt was ruining his life and happiness. He had for many years been a professor in a large university. Well liked, he was somewhat withdrawn although eager for friendship. At forty-two he fell in love with one of his students half his age, and married her.

97

Ever ready with kindness, solicitude, and determination
to fulfill every need of his mate, whom he treated as a
child wife, his peace of mind was complete. She accepted
his attention and protection as though it were a warm blanket. He was not only a lover, but also a father figure. Both
had found what seemed to be ideal, perfect, and the difference in age was irrelevant. Their harmony continued for
some five years. Then guilt unannounced confronted the
professor.

Somehow his young wife symbolized for him his own
masculinity, his sense of self-worth. Her love was the tem-
ple of his security, and he worshiped therein. But insidi-
ously doubt began to materialize in his mind, and finally
it intruded sharply like the ticking of a clock in an empty
room.

Increasingly he thought in circles. Suppose she left him?
He would be so alone without her—the world would be
empty. He was so much older. He would die first, leaving
her still a young woman. Imagining her in another man's
bed, he stifled cries as if he already spoke from the grave.
And then the fear and jealousy were offset by a deep sense
of guilt. He had not deserved her, had taken advantage of
the professor-student relationship. He looked at himself in
the mirror, noted that his body was still firm and vigorous,
but he could not ignore the sprinkling of gray hairs. God,
he muttered, I'm afraid of growing old!

Yet his wife seemed more active, more alive than ever,
cuddling warmly in his arms, often in late evening whis-
pering her sexual desires. But somehow since the gloomy
ruminations had encroached upon his mind, he found himself often unable to respond satisfactorily to his wife's in-
vitations. In fact, frequently impotency defeated him.

His sense of guilt was now compounded, feeling inadequate and unworthy of his wife. What right had he to saddle her with a man twice her age? Vibrant and in the prime of her sexual supremacy, she was tied to a man who was on the defensive, pretending that he had work to do instead of following her upstairs. But he was not working when alone, he pictured her in bed in her perfumed pajamas, her body yearning for the physical love she deserved. Fleetingly, he thought of suicide, feeling that only death could obliterate his sense of guilt.

At this crisis point, he sought help, revealing his overwhelming guilt. It became evident that the negative feeling itself was the main cause of his sexual dysfunction, feeding upon itself into further hindrance to his performance.

"I'm just too old—falling apart," he declared, eyelids drooping in his despair. "I'm fifty-four," he added as if dealing himself a blow.

It was explained firmly that age had little to do with sexual potency, which can remain as long as one's life if one is physically and emotionally healthy. "Have you had a physical exam lately?" I asked.

"Yes, of course. My doctor says there is nothing wrong, to exercise and so on."

It became obvious that this was a psychological problem involving several unmet needs. Following our interview, I asked to see his wife.

She was indeed a comely young woman, who quickly confirmed her love for her husband. In fact she was not as disturbed by her husband's sexual inadequacies as he had imagined.

"Tell me, Doctor—" she said. "I *am* a bit worried about him. He seems so depressed and nervous. Is it my fault? Can I help?"

"You certainly can," I put in encouragingly.

I explained the common needs of belonging and achievement, giving her a long list of possible things to do as you have learned in previous chapters.

Thereafter, they played golf together, engaged in fun things mutually, which increasingly gave him a sense of belonging, especially when friends were called into their activities. At every opportunity, his wife recognized anything that he did well. She showed interest in his research, encouraged him. Gradually, his research project progressed and became alive.

In other words, one person was able to do what any friend could have done, take every opportunity to make him feel wanted, to belong and also to be imbued with a sense of achievement. He was now too busy to be completely self-centered. Absorbed in new satisfying activities, his mind had little time for morbid speculations, and his mood changed from self-pity to the enjoyment of a new freedom and a feeling of self-worth. His problem gradually evaporated because in meeting other psychological needs, his desire to be free of guilt likewise was attained. He knew also that love and affection were his without further doubt.

In a later chapter, we shall examine sexual guilt more thoroughly. Suffice it to say at this point that the great majority of sexual problems and their accompanying guilt are due to unmet needs and rarely to physical causes.

Some young people feel guilty at the way they treat their parents, often regretting the behavior resented by their elders. Sometimes they reject the old ways of doing things, yet that intangible tie to the values and home still holds. The conflict often emerges as guilt, becoming part of the emotional disturbances in youth.

Parents, on the other hand, are frequently ambivalent about their children, blaming themselves when their offspring seem to have gone astray, but at the same time feeling an underlying anger. The guilt is the more painful because the parents rationalize that they could have been wiser and more effective in their duties.

Imagine the happily married man who somehow has been led into adultery, an affair with the wife of his best friend. Fearing to lose the respect of his family, his worry and guilt may permeate his whole existence.

What about the teenager who has become pregnant due to her carelessness, perhaps not being sure even of the father's name? She faces the ordeal, determined to keep her baby, live with her parents, and somehow manage. But her parents object, urge her to give up the infant for adoption. Social workers point out the difficulties of bringing up an illegitimate child in our society. She holds the baby, feeling the maternal instinct, then allows a nurse to remove it somehow to be lost in that huge world, never again for her to feel her own flesh embodied in her baby. The conflict between love of the child and the pain of yielding to the advice of others gives birth to something perhaps never forgotten, the guilt clinging to her heart like an immovable object throughout the years.

In a moment of uncontrolled anger, a man commits an act of violence against a wife, child, sibling. Few people are without conscience and guilt except those who perpetrate most of the crimes of violence, psychopathic characters. The average person cannot persistently inflict physical harm except in organized sports or athletics without having at least a tinge of guilt or a feeling of self-blame.

Paradoxically, the reverse may apply. A teenager, for example, growing up in a high crime area may seek to solve or avoid a sense of guilt in a strange way. Even though he may have an aversion to violence, he feels impelled to show cruelty in order to gain the macho image that he desires. Should he refrain from violence, he may experience a sense of guilt because he feels cowardly, unworthy of respect from his peers.

Perhaps this is the root of the seemingly unreasonable action of young people who are not satisfied only to rob, but must add the killing of innocent victims. If they did not prove that they are tough and heartless, they would forfeit the badge of ruthlessness without which they would feel guilty for not being admired by the psychopathic element about them.

Guilt has many facets, numerous compulsions and causes. It is like a multiheaded serpent striking all levels of our society, rich and poor, educated and uneducated. The human psyche suffers from it, and it sometimes destroys the very will to live.

There are steps that you can take to help others attain freedom from guilt. First you must allow the person to ventilate his guilt, talk about it, even wallow in self-blame. Through such "talking out," the victim pinpoints the guilt instead of permitting it to be generalized as free-floating anxiety. You are mainly listening. It may help, however, to ask the guilty one to express his feeling as clearly as possible. Perhaps he may say, "I'm afraid of getting old." But further inquiry may lead nearer to the core of his guilt when he says that he fears losing his wife because he feels unworthy of her. At this point, we're getting closer to the essential guilt, namely, the sense of inadequate masculinity. Thus it is desirable to peg the guilt as specifically as possible.

Share the details of your own sense of guilt, past and present, emphasizing that the other person is not alone, that all people at one time or other are the victims of guilt.

A person enmeshed in guilt has a conscious or unconscious feeling that he deserves to be punished. Various religions recognize not only confession (ventilation) but also the expectation of punishment in the form of penance. However, you can point out that a person undergoing the torture of guilt has already been punished enough.

The next step is to lessen the sense of guilt even though to many people it might seem justified. Circumstances, both environmental and psychological, may have made it nearly impossible for the person to have acted otherwise. Some moralists, of course, would assert that a person has a choice and a responsibility for right or wrong. That is merely stating that a person has the superego strength of conscience—which is not generally so. To avoid evil at all times is not given to any man.

In your efforts to lessen the sense of guilt in another person, the past must be put aside. This is not to condone evil deeds. We are now dealing with rehabilitating a person's spirit. The aim is not only to relieve emotional stress, but also perhaps to prevent the repetition of acts that led to the person's guilt in the first place. Accordingly, tell the victim that he has more important things to do than stewing over the past.

Now you are ready to use your main weapons, those of instilling a sense of belonging and a feeling of achievement. You have alraady found the effectiveness of these devices. Use them as the height of your campaign to alleviate the self-blame in others. And once more the process will redound to your advantage, indirectly tending to obliterate whatever sense of guilt you may have possessed.

You have been working on your needs for belonging and achievement and also to get rid of your fears. Now the fourth psychological need, that of eliminating guilt, has received your attention. All your psychological needs must be satisfied concurrently, never neglecting an earlier one as you proceed with the next need in our program.

Unobtrusively, as you have devoted time to helping others meet their needs, you have found out that your own frustrations were gradually reduced. And since your unmet needs were the cause of undesirable overweight, a strange transformation has been taking place. Somehow, eating no longer exerts an irresistible pull toward excess.

Chapter **X**

Love

Strange as it may seem, love can be a mask for hatred. And vice versa, hatred can be a screen obscuring the emotion of love.

This emotion called love has been dwelt upon in stories since man could talk, whether the tales were told by campfire in gloomy caves or in the dazzling colors of a Broadway opening. Few commercials on radio or television fail to exploit it, and the soap operas drip with the tears and ecstasies of love—attained or sought after. Perhaps the fascination of the emotion is because it causes as much pain as it does joy.

Wars are fought for love of country. People commit suicide because they are without love. Its intensity in some cases is like that of a comet suddenly appearing in a flash of radiance, only to disappear leaving the sky empty again. In others, it is a gradual process of recognition, like the faint glimmer of approaching dawn. Then the light of love, eternally praised in songs by poets, becomes an endless day lasting for one's lifetime.

But why is love so closely allied to hatred? Perhaps the deepest and most bitter hate is reserved for a former lover because he deprived us of something so dear. Hatred is the only weapon we have against him, a helpless retribution and vengeance.

The reverse can occur when a dictator threatens the lives

of his subjects. Under the circumstances, it is safer to love him than to hate him. This also applies to overpunitive parents. When the dictator has lost his power, he is hanged by the heels in the public square; when the cruel parent is no longer able to dominate, his children also inflict their venom on him.

But do you know when you really love? Or whether the emotion you feel is volatile, glowing momentarily like a sudden flash in the sky, with darkness and stillness to follow?

Reactive love—as previously discussed—is sudden, overpowering, showy, and often based on a neurotic foundation with no permanence. It is here today and threatens to be gone tomorrow, because it is not the love object that is sought but an avoidance of neurotic fears. The person possessed by such love is afraid of being rejected, abandoned, and grasps at love as a means of saving his tremulous soul.

Real love develops slowly. It is a gradual growth of mutual respect, a joining of aspirations, and the need to clasp another person's hand to confront life's hardships and joys together.

For Debra, it was a summer long remembered not only because she took lessons from an unusual tennis pro, but also because he fell in love with her. At first, she was greatly complimented, since every girl around the country club sought him out and flirted outrageously with him.

The summer weeks swept by with days at the beach, rides at sunset, parties, dances and—much drinking. Everything was a whirl of happiness, flying by in the glow of warm days. When Rawson, the tennis pro, met her parents, they were polite enough, though cool in their reception. Her father, a practical man, seemed disturbed by the young man, somewhat resentful of his impetuosity and open declaration of love. "It's just too fast," the father confided to his wife. "What do we know about him? Our daughter is a pretty girl, and at eighteen she looks older—but . . ." He scratched his head, puzzled and hesitant.

"Wait until the end of the season. The young man will fly south with the birds," his wife counseled.

Indeed, Florida was his next stop—and Debra was with him. A short note left on her bedroom bureau announced her hasty departure, saying, "He loves me very much, and I love him, too. Will write soon. Forgive me. I know you do not approve of him, so I must leave this way. Love, Debra."

Toward the end of January, she was back home, merely saying, "He loved me too quickly, too soon—and as quickly we realized that we were not meant for each other." And her parents respected her desire to forget the experience. The episode was dead and gone. But Florida had left its mark.

Sadder yet determined to continue her college studies, Debra avoided dating, appearing too busy to consider closeness with men on the campus. One young man, however, now an accountant, she looked upon as a friend. For years they had sailed together and shared other interests.

Finally, at twenty-one, she knew that she loved this longtime friend, and he loved her without ostentation but with respect. It had been a slowly developed closeness, a real foundation for a lifetime relationship.

In her late teens, Debra had accepted the presumption that marriage was merely words on a piece of paper. And judging from the fact that about fifty percent of marriages end in divorce, she was partly right. The real basis of a satisfying and lasting marriage is in the heart and mental stability of the participants.

Debra now realized that her first bed partner had experienced reactive love, a sudden but unstable emotion. She knew, too, that lasting love is not a temporary flash of sunshine fading quickly at the first storm clouds.

It is often said that one has to love himself before he can love another. That statement requires clarification before it can be wholly accepted. No one who is intensely self-centered, completely narcissistic, can love others. However, the statement is true in that a person must have a sense of self-worth before he can project valid love for others.

The completely selfish person may seem to have affection for another, but in fact that affection is a counterfeit, used as a means of aggrandizing his own ego and feeding his neurotic compulsions. There is no sharing in the mind of the narcissistic lover, whereas the person who possesses a realistic sense of self-worth can reach out to a love-mate with honesty and emotional maturity. Being aware of another person's needs and desiring to meet those needs is the essence of real love. Self-love, indeed, is necessary, but not to the extent that others have no part in it. Real love is a sharing, and cannot exist in the vacuum of mere self-interest.

Have you ever had the urge to return to your childhood environment, the home where you grew up? Somehow the years seem to have obliterated the pain, the scoldings, and the memories of hurts. Today, the pleasure and the joy of childhood remain, the psyche tending to forget the bad and hold on primarily to the good.

Do you remember being cruel to your sister because you loved her, shining your older brother's shoes for a nickel, your father grumbling after the day's work yet interested when you recited the excitement or disappointment of your own day? Do you remember your mother troubled in thought, worrying about the rent money, then suddenly

laughing at your antics—laughing so hard that tears came
to her eyes. Do you recall on a clear day, running headlong down the hill, imagining yourself riding with the wind
in your hair, a cowboy, brave and true on his trusty steed?

Did you ever return to the house of your childhood, deserted and paint-peeled now? You walked the creaky
boards, smelled the moldy interior, and the ghosts of yes-
teryear seemed to hover in dark corners. A sadness per-
meated the old building; but as you walked away, you
turned back for a last glance—and suddenly you heard in
your imagination a distant laughter, ringing softly. And
singing voices called full of gladness from across the years.

Yes, you can go home again. The pain goes away, being
of secondary consequence. The past moments of joy cling
within you. Home lives in distant love that comes back,
reverberating in your heart across the years.

Do you remember a teacher who inspired you? You are
lucky if out of the many you recall at least one. An un-
gainly man was one of those for me, bald, pants cuffs
drooping over his shoes. Passing him, a stranger might
have turned away in pity. But really knowing him was the
touch of magic—one of the few who live forever in the
minds of their students. Hitherto, I had merely tolerated
the study of literature. But because of his own love of
poetry, I caught his spirit of beauty and appreciation, his
ever-ready smile of goodness and playful challenge, his
unselfishness, his faith in me, and his encouragement. I
hated history but learned to love it because he loved it.

A good teacher is a person who loves his pupils, who
projects care and humor, lacks prejudice, understands, and
has the ability to inspire because of his own reaching out
for the good in people.

Where is happiness without friends? It is often illusive,
rarely gained unless it comes through others. A great artist

may labor long and hard in isolation, but without friends to praise him, he is to himself the nothingness of his own alienation. It is true that if you want a friend, you must first be willing to be one.

Some people find love in organized religion. Others reach out for it in the concept that all life is one expression of the desire to live, a blind force perhaps, but one that makes life itself holy. No religion or philosophy can be ridiculous if the aim is to receive and to give love.

The need for love is universal, from the hardened criminal to the cloistered nun. Man, woman, child, no matter how one would hide and repress that need, it lies there in the soul ever reaching for a way to realization. A man who loves can never be all bad—which is another way of saying that there is good in every person.

There are many avenues through which you can give love and its affiliates such as affection, friendship, consideration. It is at once the easiest to bestow and the hardest to convey both honestly and directly.

In your campaign to meet the need for love in others, you can go out of your way to convey that emotion, showing that you do love someone who is close to you and yet has been somewhat neglected. How much does it cost to tell someone that you love her or him—your wife, girl or boyfriend, brother, sister, mother, father? Of course, in our somewhat puzzling society, one does not fling the word about so readily, especially to one of touchy masculinity.

Love, nevertheless, is a form of friendship, respect, and appreciation of another's worth. It must be expressed tactfully without presumption on a person's sensitivity. But there are a thousand ways to show that you like people. Offer to help, to reassure, to protect when protection and reassurance seem needed. Accept the person who needs love, show that the other person is appreciated. Laugh,

and have fun together. Be concerned when the other person hurts, sympathize, take interest in the other person's
home, friends. Listen, understand, talk about discord in
his environment.

Remember people's birthdays and aniversaries, recognize special events with flowers or at least with a call. Do
not hesitate to accept gifts, for those generally are love
offerings yielding satisfaction to the giver. Touch is the
key to closeness, the secret communication of souls, the
intangible flow of one aura into another, the harbinger of
even closer things combining into full acceptance and approval of the other person.

It is obvious that if you give love, if you help others to
meet their need for affection and approval, they will in
turn tend to love you. Like the proverbial bread cast upon
the waters, love is the reward that love gives.

If you have followed suggestions for meeting the love
need of people in your milieu, in the natural course of
events you will have discovered that your own need for
this emotional satisfaction has been fulfilled. Then the
neurotic tendency to overeat almost miraculously will have
lost its disrupting influence.

Chapter **XI**

Sex

Sex, like love, is also a two-edged sword capable of wielding good as well as evil—construction as well as destruction. Sex is the ultimate need that firms up the very foundation of man's existence and civilization. It's obvious that without sex the human race would cease to be. Not so obvious but as true is that people derive a multitude of pleasures from the sex act. It is the attraction that binds man and woman. The family is cemented by sex and the children created thereby, extending outward to community and country.

Sexual dysfunctions and competitions are acknowledged, however, as the main causes of emotional disorders and mental illnesses. Many physicians, long before the psychoanalyst Sigmund Freud, had discovered the significance of sex, that its stifling, perversion, and misdirection are not without responsibility in mental, social, and even physical malfunctions. Mental disabilities, it is argued, arise from the damming up of the energy of this powerful drive.

The social problems created by sex are many, including friction among neighbors, adultery, and competition for the opposite sex. Physical ailments resulting from the sexual drive, of course, include venereal diseases and a host of psychosomatic disorders.

The sexual behavior between men and women is complicated by the differences between the two. Those differences, both physical and psychological, prevent us from speaking of equality of the sexes or superiority of one over the other. The simple fact is that women are superior to men in some respects and men are superior in others.

The differences make men muscularly stronger than women, but men tend to die earlier than women. The man has comparatively visible sex organs, whereas the woman's genitals are largely hidden within her body. Indeed, many other physical differences exist. But to say that one sex is superior to the other is ridiculous since that is comparing unlikes. Each sex excels in some category, and to seek to deny the distinctions would rob one or the other of their respective characteristics.

We can conclude, however, that the differences between the sexes are due to biological as well as cultural factors— upon which rest misunderstanding and the continuance of chauvinism on the part of males. In order to help one sex or the other to meet sexual needs there must be a greater awareness of the differences.

Early women were at a disadvantage biologically. It was the female who was rendered pregnant and was helpless immediately after giving birth. The infant had to be fed and cared for if it were to survive. The man was free to hunt or make war while his mate tended the cave fire and foraged for food close to home without the arduous treks in the forest.

Perhaps man's chauvinism was sustained in those ancient times when masculinity was in the hunt and femininity was in the comparative seclusion of home.

Pregnancy no long exacts such a toll, and man's assumed superiority over women is losing its validity. Strangely, however, women are still held at least psychologically by the notions of centuries past, and certainly that hangover is evident in the way they meet their sexual needs.

For example, the girl expects the man to take the initiative in making sexual advances. A woman goes to a singles bar expecting to be picked up, while the man concentrates on doing the selecting. It is true that with the so-called sexual revolution changes have occurred. Often now the liberated "weaker sex" does not hesitate to make her sexual desires known.

A man may be fascinated by a *Playboy* centerfold photo. The woman, on the other hand, is comparatively little interested in male nudity. The male in his ignorance assumes that the opposite sex is as quickly aroused as he, not realizing that she prefers foreplay and loving words before union and that her sexual need is quite different from his own. Female frigidity can result from this lack of knowledge.

Conversely, with the increasing liberation of woman, she may demand her right to be the aggressor, making sexual demands on her partner. The man may find himself threatened by this change in order, seeing it as an attack on his masculinity—with the result sometimes that he cannot achieve an erection. In both sexes, ignorance of the other's sexual needs often breeds resentment and dysfunction.

The conflicts about sexual problems are particularly severe among teenagers. It seems that whatever course of action is selected leaves them with a dilemma of doubt, guilt, and confusion. For instance, if the teenager choses to be active sexually, he or she behaves contrary to the expectations and norms of parents and society, which still frown on premarital sex, particularly among teenagers. The conscience, rebelled against, makes many of them uncomfortable, especially if parents are respected and loved.

On the other hand, young people who abstain from sexual contacts are aware of their own mounting tension during the years when their whole biological apparatus cries for fulfillment and expression. The pressure of their less reserved peers is immense. They seem to enjoy their social life, with more dates and a devil-may-care existence. Many enter the drug scene with its sexual ally of rebellion, arousing possibly reluctant envy on the part of their straighter fellows.

To yield to temptation is to cast aside old values, the criteria of parents and the more sedate part of society. But the pleasure of freer sex and its enticements are at times overwhelming. If you do not have sex with your boyfriend, he might leave you. You feel an outcast because "everyone else is doing it." Give in and be "with it," and you feel you have betrayed the home and other institutions that have nurtured you.

When we read the report that fifty-one percent of illegitimate births are from teenagers, the conclusion might be too readily accepted that young people have been liberated sexually. It is true that the sexual revolution has brought many people to be more open-minded. Yet it would be false to conclude that the majority of teenagers are active sexually. The fact is that conflicts in this area continue to plague many young people and are part of their pressures and ambivalence as they tentatively cross the threshold into adulthood.

Nevertheless, the sex drive must have an outlet. It is a force that cannot be denied indefinitely without harm to health and personality. If this statement seems an exaggeration of reality, it is offset by the fact that there are several ways to express sexuality to suit circumstances and the desire of the individual. These are first, active expression by intercourse, second, self-release of tension, and third, sublimation of the instinctual drive. All of these, or a combination, are used to prevent the building up of undue sexual pressures.

Active Expression   Possibly the most prevalent means of sexual relief is standard intercourse between partners, but there are problems even here. Ninety-five percent of difficulties in normal sex relationships are due to psychological blocks or conflicts, resulting in impotency, premature ejaculation, frigidity, and inability to have an orgasm. These are effectively treated by sex therapists. Yet it is evident that the methods utilized are aimed toward establishing self-worth, self-confidence, and the change in circumstances to attain that sense of self-acceptance. Since this whole book is devoted to the meeting of other psychological needs as well as sexual fulfillment, it must follow that the recommendations herein presented will help to improve the personality as a whole and thus to increase the pleasure of the sex drive in both the healthy and the emotionally disturbed. Later in this chapter we will give more specific directions to help others meet their sexual needs.

Self-release   It was the custom early in this century for the medical profession to denounce masturbation, then called self-abuse. The practice was deemed responsible for insanity, a host of physical illnesses—and sending you straight to hell.

Yet ninety-nine percent of men admit to masturbation at one time or other—and cynics suggest that the remaining one percent lie about it. It is likely that a longtime frigid woman is one who has never masturbated, who is inhibited and unable to experience the potential sensation of her own body, later frustrated in not being able to experience the ecstasy of satisfactory intercourse.

It is now admitted that there is no physical harm in masturbation, and for those who cannot find another suitable outlet, it need not be a source of guilt.

Sublimation   It has been noted that the sex drive should have an outlet. That means not that one must engage in physical activities of a sexual nature, but that the process of sublimation can be substituted, the channeling of sexual energy into other activities and aims.

To say that chastity is unnatural if not harmful is to neglect the fact that one can be perfectly happy without outward expression of sex. Sublimation can be a satisfactory replacement. Thousands upon thousands of people throughout the world have taken vows of chastity, and mental illness is not more prevalent among these men and women of the church. Rather they appear happier in many instances as compared to the average population. These people have traded worldly pleasures for a more worthy purpose in their estimation. Their sublimation is complete, and it succeeds in making their lives worthwhile.

Sublimation is also a tool for greater contentment through one's sense of achievement, creative expression in a profession, art, music, family, and daily tasks. Each person can reach sexual expression through sublimation for his own good and that of others.

However, for those who choose a different route to sexual expression, there are many things you can do to help them meet their sex need. Perhaps guilt is too frequently linked to erotic fantasies. Most of this guilt is based on ignorance or has been programmed by unwise parents and teachers through excessive control and discipline of the child. This discipline, of course, arises from the concept that sex is dirty and unnatural except under limited circumstances.

Part of your campaign must therefore be toward the truth, that guilt in sexual matters is unjustified when no harm is done to others. It is advisable to point out that most sexual difficulties are caused by a lack of self-esteem, a sense of inadequacy that can be changed by new attitudes.

You can, of course, start with your own mate, applying your efforts to satisfy his or her need. Have firmly in mind that your help and guidance are capable of facilitating guiltless and pleasurable sexual relationships.

The blocking of the sex need is strikingly exemplified in the fact that half the male population have a problem with sexual potency at one time or other, and a considerable number are unable to have an erection at any time. Thirty percent of women who engage in premarital sex are not able to have an orgasm, while ten percent after ten years of marriage are still inorgastic.

Apart from helping your mate, sex education to the extent presented in this chapter can convey to others means of facilitating their sex adjustment.

What are the guidelines, in addition to those already specified, that can help make sex more fulfilling?

The ability to abandon yourself to the sex act is of paramount importance. There should be a sense of security on the part of each partner. Communication should be open, frank, and without guilt, needs and desires disclosed honestly without shame.

It should be emphasized that your partner should never be criticized, since anything negative tends to lessen potency and excitement. The atmosphere should reflect trust and relaxation. Take your time. Foreplay, kisses, and caresses pay off in a more satisfying experience. Respect and praise, rather than confrontation, enhance the feeling of security and anticipation. The relationship should be nondemanding, allowing each partner to react at ease and pleasurably.

It becomes evident that by tact and understanding in the satisfaction of the sexual needs of others, you reap the reward of meeting your own, proving again that by helping others to discover their potentialities and self-realization you become the recipient of adjustment within yourself. And in the process your body will no longer abandon itself to a pudgy figure as a means of lessening anxiety and frustration.

Chapter **XII**

Understanding

You began by wanting to lose weight, most likely after repeated failures utilizing methods that didn't work. The recommendations made herein seemed so unusual that you were skeptical—especially when you were informed that the problem of losing weight should be forgotten for the time being. By a seemingly magic process—more specifically, a psychological one—you would achieve your goal of slimness with comparatively little effort.

What happened if you followed directions for a reasonable length of time—or what will occur if you persist in the program?

Your life now takes a completely new slant. You realize that compulsive eating is a defensive device sought when you feel bored, rejected, abandoned, fearful, guilty, self-hated, or depressed. Then you observe that these destructive feelings arise because psychologically you are being deprived of needs that are required for your peace of mind and well-being.

As your psychological needs are met through specific recommendations, you discover that the urge to overeat has disappeared or at least lessened, since the defense against frustration and anxiety is no longer needed. You eat now to replenish your energy, and not to feed a neurotic urge for oral gratification. In short, you have become more secure, and accordingly have no more compulsion to stuff yourself purely for release of tension. You are no longer compelled to fight off anxieties because most of them have already disappeared—and strangely the poundage, too, slowly but steadily.

Philosophical Slant

There are three main outlooks on life, one of complete selfishness; another of the opposite, namely, complete unselfishness; and a third comprising a combination of the two. In other words, you cannot be solely preoccupied with yourself, nor should you be concerned only with the welfare of others, forgetting about your own needs.

Complete Selfishness   The narcissistic type of person soon discovers that he loses contact with others and ultimately finds himself alone. The world passes him by, leaving him alienated even from himself in the end. His little palace of self-pride finally crumbles because no real love and companionship exist therein—only the loneliness remains.

Yet the purely selfish person can manipulate people as though from afar. History tells of great conquerors laying waste country after country without feelings for the havoc wreaked. The monuments to their conquests have been obliterated by time, leaving only the fading memory of those who wished to conquer the world because they had never conquered themselves.

Even in your comparatively small battle with overweight, you, too, have lost because you concentrated too much on yourself and not enough on others. All the concoctions, the pills, and even the excruciating bulimia and anorexia nervosa were in vain because you thought only of yourself, not realizing that self-growth can come only by linking your life to others.

Complete Unselfishness   On the contrary, the unselfish person detaches himself from his own identity. One must, as previously noted, have a sense of self-worth before one can love others.

It might seem that we should exclude the dedicated person who gives his life to religious aims. But it may be that such a person is not really completely unselfish, since salvation and heaven await him as a personal reward.

Certainly, complete unselfishness tends to alienate the self self because the person and his needs are generally overlooked. Often the unselfishness is a defense against a guilt-filled tendency to the opposite inclination. A highly successful businessman who has made millions through sharp deals may in old age be judged wholly unselfish because of his philanthropy. And yet the man may be acting most selfishly by giving away his money in an effort to atone for past wrongs and transgressions. Behind the unselfishness may lurk an unconscious self-interest.

Fortunately, complete unselfishness regardless of motive is advantageous for those receiving its bounties. A woman travels to far countries and seeks to serve in backward cultures, endangering her health but persisting despite great difficulties seemingly without thanks or reward. If, however, the person gives her life away as a means of escaping unbearable guilt, she rarely succeeds, but becomes detached from her self-identity. She has lost herself in the sea of humanity, and her isolation amidst the many is complete. She has purchased the outside world at the price of losing her inner self.

If one cannot reach happiness except through others, so

it is equally true that a similar state of mind cannot be attained without interest in one's own welfare.

Synthesis Interest   The wisest course is to merge and combine self-interest with those of others. It is a binding or synthesis of your own needs with those of people with whom you come in contact. When a person thinks of both himself and others to regulate his conduct, he creates a balance between himself and the world outside. An equilibrium is established, a sort of rhythm linked to nature itself.

If a man is concerned purely with his own selfishness, the balance is skewed toward isolation, and he loses empathy for others. Being egocentric, he finds himself increasingly alone. He has no real friends, since they soon discover that they are mere tools in a selfish game.

On the other hand, the person who is concerned only with the welfare of others is now detached from himself. Neglecting his own person, he proves finally unable to help others because of a tendency to lessen the link between himself and the world.

Thus, in order to be effective in dealing with human welfare, more than egoism or absolute altruism is required. There must be a merging of the two, putting the person in tune with his fellowmen while not neglecting his own needs. He is no longer alone, but rather synchronized with the vast network of the common good. He plays a part as a self-interested person who also accepts some responsibility for his neighbors. He becomes a teammate in the human drama.

Now you have become more aware of and understand more clearly the unusual method prescribed in this program of weight control. It is true that you were told not to think of yourself at the beginning in order to gradually release you from the neurotic framework under which you operated. However, you soon discovered that self-interest was only temporarily postponed; and certainly you knew that the primary objective was the solution of your weight problem. You were led to assume both the egoistic and the altruistic approaches practically at the same time. By helping others to meet their psychological needs, you satisfied your own—and this was your real objective.

Lo and behold, you have served yourself well, meeting the justified desires of others while at the same time reaping the compensation of getting what you wanted. Incidentally, that itself is a means not only of losing weight, but also of gaining mental health. It may prove to be a vehicle by which you can obtain many things that hitherto have been beyond your reach. It might be termed the golden key to happiness and self-worth.

Common-sense Psychology

Although the principles enunciated here have a solid base in research that establishes their validity, we have avoided psychological jargon, trusting instead to common sense to evaluate the thesis and the reasons for the course of action recommended.

As a whole, you need not be convinced that frustration is the cause of emotional discomforts. You have only to look back on your own experience. If you are denied something that you want dearly, there occurs an uneasiness, a tension. Frustration, indeed, arouses anxiety.

This resultant anxiety makes you feel that somehow it should be removed for your peace of mind. And so at this point you have several choices open to you. One course of action may incline toward self-defeating behavior involving several emotional states. First you may become angry, then guilty, followed by self-blame, and finally by depression. This we called the Wheel of Despair because each rung deepens the difficulties and the inability to deal with the discontentment.

On the other hand, you might choose to solve your problem in a mature way, seeking to remove the frustration by meeting your basic psychological needs, including a sense of belonging and of achievement, freedom from guilt and from fear, and a need for love or for sex.

The plan recommended herein involves recognizing your negative feelings, then determining to remove the cause by practicing means of fulfilling your basic needs.

Have you ever considered that even physical illnesses may be caused by frustrations? An artery, for example, is narrowed by a blood clot. This prevents sufficient nourishment from reaching the heart or the brain. In other words, the frustration imposed by the blood clot results in illness that must be eliminated by medication or surgery—removing the frustration. Similarly, the body is frustrated in its smooth functioning by an invasion of destructive bacteria or viruses. Removing the frustration caused by these factors through medication or the body's natural countermeasures is followed by improved health. Ponder on the function of frustration in all diseases. In each case, your intelligence can tell you that the lack of something or the presence of a condition serves to limit the body's ability to function in a normal and healthy way.

Now we come back again to the fact that you want to lose weight. Your overweight may be only enough to make you feel that you might be more attractive by taking off a few pounds. Nothing is more beautiful than a well-proportioned body. Accordingly, the goal of reaching that ideal is not unworthy of your aspiration.

You may, however, have become really obese. The fat is evidence of regression, a yielding to oral compulsion and resignation. A series of frustrations, denials, and psychological deprivations may have led to indifference to your own fate.

But by meeting your needs as prescribed, there is light and a solution ahead. You really can become slim, admirable in the figure that you desire. Indeed, you will lose weight because now you know why you sought food in excessive quantities. And an amazing result of this process will emerge as a precious by-product: a basic change in your personality, a new outlook on life with richness little realized in the past.

Oh, I almost forgot to tell you. When your psychological needs have been met, you can go on a reasonable diet. But this time it will not be a sole response to frustration and anxiety. The compulsive and neurotic urge to overeat will no longer be there, having been replaced by an unmixed desire for self-improvement.

May you realize your dream of a happier and more beautiful body.

Chapter XIII

For Those Underweight

This book has been almost entirely slanted toward persons concerned with losing weight. Although the number of underweight people is small in comparison, nevertheless they are frequently equally troubled, dissatisfied, and disturbed by thinness sometimes bordering on emaciation. Such people are actually tormented, ashamed of their thin legs, small bosom—or in men lack of muscular development.

These people also need guidance and help in the attainment of better figures. They are entitled to a workable course of action to remedy their shortcomings, to share in a brighter future.

First, we shall examine briefly the sources or causes of their sense of inadequacy. Second, we shall point out the changes in behavior necessary to bring about a realization of a happier condition. But it must be reemphasized that underweight, like overweight, is generally not due to physical factors but rather to psychological causes. Fatness and thinness are in the vast majority of cases mere symptoms of deeper emotional dynamics.

It has been explained that practically all neurotic disorders are caused by frustrations, the inability to meet one's psychological needs. It has also been stated that obesity is a defense against the anxiety aroused by the unmet needs. Thinness may be a response to the same mechanism.

But why does one person react to anxiety by allowing himself to become fat while another reacts by becoming too thin for comfort or peace of mind?

Let us examine some of the dynamics involved in the process of becoming too thin.

Imprints

As the term implies, there are ideas implanted early in life by parents or other authority figures. This occurs through remarks made casually or in anger, which become subtle but powerful commands or compulsions that later influence one's behavior.

For example, the mother might say that Linda has been skinny since birth and probably will always be scrawny. If comments of this nature, even made without conscious intent, are repeated on a variety of occasions, then Linda, confronted in adult life with frustrations that she cannot master, will tend to make the prophecy come true. The idea of being thin has been embedded deep in her subconscious, and she now finds herself refusing food in sufficient quantities, regressing to the earlier stage when the accusation of thinness implied reproach.

Common sense tells us that we are all influenced by early ideas implanted by parents. The derogatory remarks remain, forgotten but lurking, to be reactivated under stress. Under this process, the thin person has unconsciously selected underweight as a response to acute or chronic disappointment.

Past Experiences

Imprints derive their power from something we have been told. Past experiences are events through which we have lived. Because of their emotional intensity, they have left marks in our psyche. The person anticipates that similar situations will produce like results. For instance, suppose a child was frequently sent to bed without supper, deprived of nourishment as a punishment for naughtiness. Repetition of this sequence would inevitably establish a link between loss of love and being denied food. Later in life, the adult experiencing loss of love, abandonment, disappointments, can reestablish the linkage, the masochistic urge to abstain from sufficient nourishment.

Secondary Gain

Sometimes the underweight person derives some satisfaction from his thinness. Strange as it may seem, a person can actually persist in maintaining a malign condition because he feels that he is thereby rewarded. Mary, a high school student, for example, was thin and almost gaunt. Yet no matter how persistently food was pressed upon her by her mother, she remained close to emaciation. Throughout Mary's childhood, her mother had been worried about her, obsessed with the idea that she was too thin, too susceptible to colds and other illnesses.

Being a skinny kid became in Mary's mind a means by which she obtained more love and attention from her mother. Much as Mary was troubled by her frail body, the perpetuation of her condition assured the continuation of the mother's solicitude, a triumph for Mary who could thus receive more attention than her siblings.

Identification

A person may manifest the symptom of underweight because of an identification with some important figure who is also thin. The person thus imitated is usually a member of the family, a character from a book, or a figure in movies or television. For example, a young girl may admire fashion models whose bodies are little more than clothes racks.

Conflicts

The underweight person may have a desire for something prohibited by parents, society, or his own inner feelings. Thinness then either prevents carrying out the desire or is a symbolic fulfillment of the desire. A young girl, for example, was troubled by sexual desires. Making her body unattractive and skinny was a subconscious way to avoid tempting the opposite sex. This twisted process was accompanied by a fantasy that by her being helpless and weak someday a prince charming would awaken her from her trouble with a magic kiss.

Self-punishment

It is often the case that underweight serves primarily as a means of self-punishment for some present or forgotten sin. This may be intended either to relieve guilt feelings or to avoid harsher punishment from some higher authority. An example could be guilt for self-stimulation or other sexual acts that the person wrongly considers sinful.

A case in point is a young man who had incestuous desire for his mother—a desire that he put aside in horror. He nevertheless felt that he should be punished and responded with neglect of his body, as if by deprivation he could exorcise the unacceptable urge. By making himself as small as possible, he seemed to deny his manhood, which he deemed the cause of his evil thoughts; and he also endowed this maneuver of underweight with self-inflicted punishment.

Several examples of the psychological causes of being consistently too thin have been presented to show possible hidden motives for behavior that is conducive to unhappiness.

These hidden influences, as in all neurotic behavior, are accompanied by anxiety, anger, guilt, self-hate, depression, and alienation on the Wheel of Despair described earlier.

Assuming, then, that underweight is your problem, the question must be: How can I resolve my dilemma and acquire the physique that I want and deserve?

The answer is in the theme of this book. All emotional difficulties, the neuroses such as compulsions, obsessions, unexplained fears, self-defeating behavior—including obesity and its opposite, thinness—are due to frustrations. The conclusion is very simple. You must work to remove as many sources of frustration as possible through the devices explained and recommended in Part Two of this book.

Reread the directions for meeting your needs. It does not matter whether you want to lose weight or to gain. Both the fat person and the thin one have responded each in his way to frustrations. Fulfilling unmet needs will remove the obstacles to better days. As you read the preceding chapters, merely replace the word overweight with underweight. And then allow your body to adjust itself to the equilibrium belonging to those who have acquired peace of mind.